Contents

Mathematics

Cursive Writing

Grammar and Reading

Social Studies

Science

Art

$$\begin{array}{r} 18.71 \\ 2\overline{)2175} \\ \underline{2} \\ 017 \\ \underline{16} \\ 015 \\ \underline{14} \\ 01 \end{array}$$

1. Find the value of **x**.

   $x + 23 = 55$

   $x = 35$

   (handwritten work: 3 2, 2 3, 5 5)

2. Find the value of **t**.

   $3 \times 8 = t + 15$

   $t = 9$

3. What is the pattern rule?

   2, 5, 11, 23, 47, 95

   The diffrence Between each numbe dublas

4. What will be the 8th term of this pattern?

   400, 385, 370, 355, 340 *325, 310, 295*

   293

5. Write the first three numbers of this pattern rule.

   start at 3, multiply by 2

   6, 12, 24

1. If there are 25 apples in each basket, how many apples are in 11 baskets?

   275 apples in each basket

   (handwritten work: 25 × 11, 25, 250, 275)

2. Order these numbers from least to greatest.

   2   1   3
   28 989, 28 229, 28 998

3. Find the product:

   125 × 0.1

   12.5

4. Write this number in words.

   234 340

   two thirty four thousand three hundred forty.

5. If 3 novels cost $21.75, how much is one novel?

   $7.25

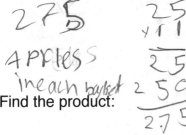

Wednesday Geometry

1. Draw a parallelogram.

2. What kind of triangle is this?

A. scalene B. right C. equilateral

3. Flip this shape

4. How many lines of symmetry are there in a rectangle?

2 lines

5. Is this an acute, obtuse or right angle?

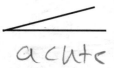

acute

Thursday Measurement

1. 3 km = 300 cm

2. 700 mm = 7000 km

3. What unit of measure would you use to measure the height of a building?

A. km B. m C. cm

4. Find the area of a rectangle with the dimensions of 8 m by 7 m.

15 m.

5. Find the perimeter of this rectangle.

1.2
2.2
2.2
1.2
____
6.8

6.8

1.2 m

2.2 m

2.2 m

1.2

© Chalkboard Publishing

Martin loved to read the sports section of the newspaper on the weekend because it gave an updated list of the local high school teams standings. Here are this week's standings in basketball:

Team	Points Scored
Panthers	68
Pumas	62
Tigers	59
Giraffes	50
Ravens	50
Mustangs	28
Stingrays	26

Use the information in the table to answer the following questions.

1. What is the range of the data? _____ 3)3 _____

2. What team is leading in points scored? _____ it scored 68 _____

3. What is the mean of the data? _____ to tell you how much teams scored _____

4. What is the mode? _____ Panthers, Pumas, Tigers, Graffes, Ravens, mustangs, stingrets _____

5. What is the best kind of graph to display this data? _____ this graph _____

BRAIN STRETCH

Identify each number as either **prime (P)** or **composite (C)**.

1. 68 __C__

2. 87 __C__

3. 9 __P__

4. 23 __P__

5. 44 __P__

6. 100 __C__

Monday — Patterning and Algebra

1. Show the first three numbers of this pattern.

   start at 3, multiply by 10

   <u>30</u>, <u>300</u>, <u>3000</u>

2. $888 \div 8 =$ 111

3. Complete the pattern.

   25, 125, 225, 325, <u>425</u>, 525

4. Create a growing pattern.

   1, 2, 4, 8, 16, 32, 64

5. What will be the 9th figure in this pattern?

9th ◇

Tuesday — Number Sense

1. List these numbers in order from least to greatest.

   19 912, 9129, 9291

   3   3   2

2. Write $876.90 in words.

   Eight hundred seventy six point ninety

3. Choose >, <, or =.

   2.24 < 2.42

4. Order these fractions from least to greatest.

   3   1   4   2

   $\frac{4}{8}$ $\frac{7}{8}$ $\frac{1}{8}$ $\frac{5}{8}$

5.

   $50 \overline{)4050}$

Wednesday — Geometry

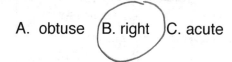

1. How many faces does a triangular prism have?

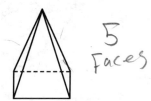
5 Faces

2. What is an angle of 90° called?

   A. obtuse B. right C. acute

3. Name this shape.

rombas

4. How many vertices does an octagon have?

8

5. Draw an obtuse angle.

Thursday — Measurement

1. Hannah trims her hair every four months. If she last cut it in May, in what month should she schedule her next haircut?

   september

2. Which would take longer, crossing the street or baking a cake?

   baking a cake

3. 5 L = 500 ml

4. How many decades in 130 years?

   13 decades

5. Compare the following using: >, < or =

   2 months [<] 65 days

Mr. McLean's math class measured the height of each student. Here are the results:

Larry 125 cm	Susan 140 cm
Martin 156 cm	Monique 129 cm
Neesha 148 cm	Naomi 132 cm
Sam 141 cm	Baxter 159 cm
Lashia 138 cm	Liam 160 cm
Stuart 155 cm	Cameron 161 cm
Camille 129 cm	Ethan 142 cm
Nathaniel 142 cm	Corrine 158 cm
Kate 135 cm	Shamila 142 cm
Nancy 129 cm	Daniel 140 cm

Use the data listed to answer these questions:

1. How many students are in the sample? _20_

2. What is the range of the data? _mr. MacLeans students_

3. What is the mode? _Cameron 61cm_

4. Who is the tallest? _Cameron._

BRAIN STRETCH

David and his 2 brothers were given $30 each. How much money do they have altogether?

900 $|

Monday | Patterning and Algebra

1. 100 ÷ 10 = _10_

2. 300 - 199 = _101_

3. Complete the pattern.

   99, 88, 77, 66, _55_, _44_, 33

4. Write the first three numbers of this pattern:

   start at 3, multiply by 5

   _15, 75, 325_

5. Fill in the blank to make the equation true.

   25 x _3_ = 200 - 125

Tuesday | Number Sense

1. Ten packs of gum cost $12.90. How much is one pack?

   _1.29_

2. What fraction is shaded?

   $\frac{6}{10} = \frac{3}{5}$

3. 34.2 x 10

   342
   x 10
   000
   3420
   342.0

4. Order these numbers from greatest to least.

   1001, 1101, 1011, 1110

   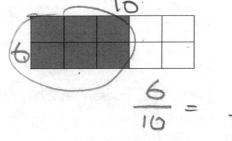

5. Round 1299 to the nearest 10.

   _1300_

Wednesday Geometry

1. What is the name of this shape?

trapazod

2. How many lines of symmetry does this letter have?

2

3. Are these shapes congruent or similar?

congruent

4. A rhombus is a polygon with how many sides?

6

5. Draw an acute angle.

Thursday Measurement

1. 40 weeks = ___ months   *60*

2. 690 dm = ___ m   *69*

3. What is the area of a square with 2 cm sides?

4

4. How many days in 2 years?

730

365
365
270

5. A can of soda usually has:

   A. 1000 ml

   B. 355 ml

   C. 10 ml

© Chalkboard Publishing

Georgina surveyed her classmates and friends to see what kind of movies they liked to watch for her media literacy class. Here are her results:

Comedy	Horror	Drama	Animation
卌 卌 卌 卌 ||| *23*	卌 卌 |||| *14*	卌 卌 ||| *13*	卌 卌 卌 卌 *20*

23
14
13
20
—
70

1. What is the most popular type of movie? _____comeautior_____

2. What is the least popular type of movie? _____Drama_____

3. What is the range of the data? _____movies_____

4. How many people did she survey? _____70_____

5. What could her survey question have been?
_____wich movie would you prefer_____

BRAIN STRETCH

State the place value of the underlined digit in each number:

1. 314 098 _____4000_____

2. 31 458 _____50_____

3. 90 738 _____90060_____

4. 961 273 _____3_____

5. 576 239 _____7000_____

6. 216 892 _____20000_____

Monday — Patterning and Algebra

1. Extend the pattern.

   500, 496, 492, <u>488</u>, <u>484</u>, <u>480</u>

2. What are the first three numbers of this pattern?

   start at 30, add 8

   ____ , ____ , ____

3. What is the pattern rule of this pattern?

   3, 12, 48, 192, 768

4. What should replace the ____ to make the following equation true?

   20
   or
   <u>48</u> + 34 = 50 - 2

   20
   34
   50

5. Complete the equivalent fraction.

   $\frac{3}{8} = \frac{8}{24}$

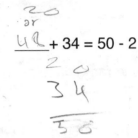

Tuesday — Number Sense

1. Round 5633 to the nearest hundred.

   5 600

2. Write all of the factors for 14.

   1, 14;
   prime

3. What number comes just after 1126?

   1127

4. Draw the money needed to represent $14.98 using the fewest number of coins and bills.

5. Choose >, <, or =.

   120.3 <u>=</u> 120.3

Wednesday | Geometry

Handwritten at top:
3 tri -- 1 -- uni
7 -- dua dual
4 quaud. -- duo
5 penta --
6 hexa --
7. Septa --
8. Octa --
9. nona
10. Deca

1. What 3D figure does this object look like?

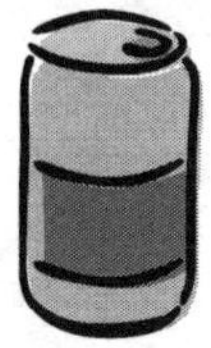

A. cube   B. sphere   (C. cylinder)

2. Look at the shapes. Choose flip, slide or turn.

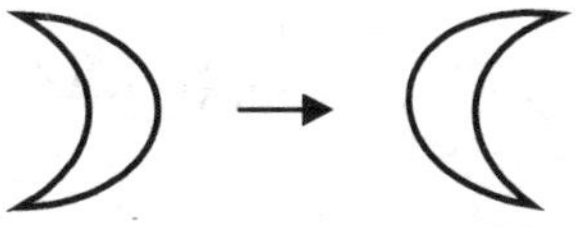

A. flip   B. slide   C. turn

3. What 3D shape can you make with this net?

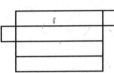 

Handwritten: regtangelsquare

4. What is the name of this shape?

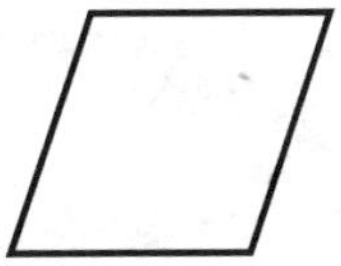

5. What is a quadrilateral?

Thursday | Measurement

1. 8.9 ml = ___0.89___ cl

Handwritten:
1 litre = 1000ml,
1 cl = 10ml,
8.9ml = 0.0089 ml.

2. The time is 10:43 pm. What time will it be in 21 minutes?

Handwritten: 11:04

3. Which has a greater volume, a kitchen garbage can or a can of soda pop?

Handwritten: garbage can

4. Find the perimeter of the trapezoid.

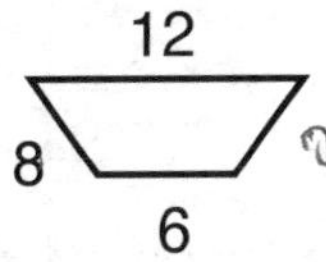

Handwritten: 16 / 12 / ___ / 28 and 34, 100

5. Complete the following using >,< or =:

1 century [>] 97 years

Megan and Kaitlyn are playing with a six sided number cube.

1. How many possible outcomes are there? ___6___

2. What is one of the possible outcomes? ___1___

3. What is the probability of rolling an odd number? ___3 out of 6___
   = ½   or 50%

4. What is the probability of rolling an even number? ___3 out of 6___

5. What is the probability of rolling a six? ___1 out of 6___
   1/6   .

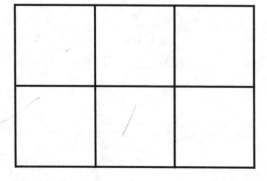

BRAIN STRETCH

How many squares can you find below?

6

1. Create a repeating pattern.

2. Fill in the blank to make the equation true.

$$36 \div 6 = 2 \times \underline{3}$$

3. What is the pattern rule?

37, 33, 29, 25, 21, 17

– 4

4. Fill in the missing numbers:

7, 12, 17, 22, 27, 32

5. What kind of pattern is this?

99, 88, 77, 66, 55, 44

A. repeating   B. growing   C. shrinking

Tuesday Number Sense

1. What fraction is not shaded?

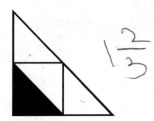

$1\frac{2}{3}$

2. Order these numbers from least to greatest.

782, 872, 702, 827

702, 782, 827, 872

3. How many eggs in 5 dozen?

A. 60 eggs

B. 72 eggs

C. 56 eggs

4. Write the numeral for:

nine thousand four hundred and seventy-one

9471

5. Write $77.35 in words.

© Chalkboard Publishing

1. What is the name of this 3D figure?

 clinder

2. What shape is the face of a cylinder?

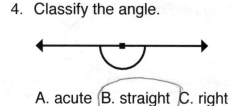

3. How many vertices does a triangle have?

 3

4. Classify the angle.

A. acute B. straight C. right

5. How many lines of symmetry does this shape have?

 10

Thursday Measurement

1. What measuring tool would you use to measure the length of a summer holiday?

A. calendar B. scale C. ruler

2. What is the perimeter of a square that has 2.4 mm sides?

3. How many weeks in 6 years?

72 weeks

4. What is the best estimate of the mass of Sara's eyeglasses?

A. 100 g
B. 100 mg
C. 100 kg

5. 12 m = 1200 mm

Answer these questions with one of the following possibilities:

impossible   unlikely   likely   certain

1. How likely is it to snow this winter? _certain_

2. How likely is it to rain this summer? _likely_

3. How likely are you to brush your teeth today? _certain_

4. How likely are you to use the telephone today? _likely_

5. How likely are you to read a book today? _certain_

6. How likely are you to watch T.V. today? _impossible_

BRAIN STRETCH

1. 53
   x 45
   265
   2120
   2385

2. 72
   x 63
   216
   4320
   4536

3. 6.1
   x 3.2
   122
   1830
   1952

4. 3.7
   x 2.2
   64
   740
   804

5. 8.4
   x 8.5
   1470
   6720
   7190

© Chalkboard Publishing

1. __40__ - 67 = 21

2. Create a growing pattern.

   7, 10, 12, 13, 15

3. Complete the pattern:

   6, 12, 24, 48, __56__, __112__

4. Fill in the blank to make this equation true.

   66 − 40 = 13 x __2__

5. What is the pattern rule?

   50, 49, 47, 44, 40, 35, 29

1. List all the factors for 40.

2. Draw the money needed to represent this amount, using the fewest number of bills and coins.

   $50.23

3. Order these fractions from least to greatest:

   5/9,   2/9,   7/9

4. 693.1 ÷ 100 =

5. Write 8954 in words.

Wednesday Geometry

1. How many lines of symmetry does this letter have?

D |

2. Is this a net for a cube?

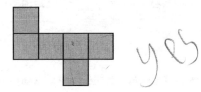 yes

3. What is this 3D figure called?

 cube

4. Is a 34 degree angle obtuse, acute or right?

x acute

5. How many edges does a cube have?

8

Thursday Measurement

1. What measurement tool would you use to find the length of a music lesson?

A. clock (B. scale) C. calendar

2. What is the year 1 decade after 1978?

1988

3. What is the perimeter of this irregular polygon?

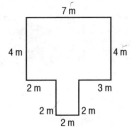 23m

7 m
4 m 4 m
2 m 3 m
2 m 2 m
2 m

4. 22 cm = 2 mm

5. How long might it take to comb your hair?

A. 1 hour (B. 1 minute) C. 1 day

Match the math term with its definition.

A. Probability   B. Mean   C. Data   D. Graph   E. Bar Graph

F. Median   G. Range   H. Pictograph   I. Mode   J. Circle Graph

1. __B__ found by dividing the sum of the numbers by the number of numbers in the set.

2. __F__ the middle number in a set of numbers arranged in order.

3. __I__ the value that occurs most often in a set of data.

4. __D__ a visual representation of data.

5. __J__ a graph in which a circle is used to display data.

6. __H__ a graph that uses pictures to display data.

7. __C__ facts or information.

8. __A__ a number from zero to one that shows how likely it is that an event will happen.

9. __E__ a graph made up of horizontal or vertical bars.

10. __G__ the difference between the smallest value and the greatest value in set of data.

BRAIN STRETCH

Write these numbers in expanded form.

1. 132 547 _____   2. 33 651 _____

3. 94 830 _____   4. 191 234 _____

1. Fill in the missing number:

   121, 123, 125, _127_ ,129, 131

2. What is the pattern rule?

   1, 11, 21, 31, 41, 51

   Start at 1 add 10 each time.

3. 1001 - 54 = 947

4. Write the first three numbers in this pattern:

   start at 72, add 8

   80, 88, 96

5. 346 = 700 - 354

   1001
   - 54
   947

   700
   - 346
   354

1. Write as a numeral:

   six hundred fifty-five thousand twelve

2.
   $3\overline{)3699}$

3. Round 1982 to the nearest ten.

4.
   3477
   - 2913

5. Mr. Davis has 31 students and 80 pieces of pizza. Each student is going to have the same amount to eat. How many pieces can each student have?

Wednesday Geometry

1. What is the name of this 3D figure?

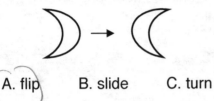 clinder

2. How many faces does a square based pyramid have?

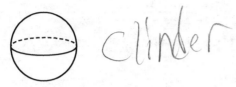 5

3. Look at the shapes. Choose flip, slide or turn.

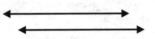

A. flip   B. slide   C. turn

4. How many sides does a rhombus have?

4

5. Classify the following pair of lines.

A. intersecting   B. parallel   C. perpendicular

Thursday Measurement

1. Michael watches 1hr and 30 minutes of TV before bedtime. If he goes to bed at 9 pm, when does he start to watch TV? How many hours does he watch in a week?

2. What is the perimeter of a heptagon with 9 m sides?

3. What is the answer in grams?

3642 g + 67 mg + 6879 g =

4. Megan can type 31 words per minute. How many words can she type in 2 hours?

5. 6820 g = _____ kg

Week 7

Here is the number of students in grades 4, 5, and 6 at Clara Breton Public School.

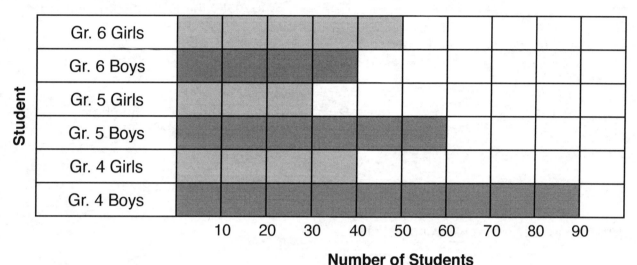

Number of Students

1. How many students are there in grades 4, 5, and 6 altogether?_____

2. How many boys are there? ___190___

3. How many girls are there? _____

4. What type of graph is this? _____

5. Which grade has more girls than boys? ___6___

BRAIN STRETCH

Marianne spent 3 hours at swim practice each week.

1) How many hours a year does she practice swimming?

2) How many hours will she have practised in 10 years?

Monday — Patterning and Algebra

1. What will be the 11th number in this pattern?

    100, 96, 92, 88, 84

2. What should replace the _____ to make the following equation true?

    $9 + 2 = 66$ _____ 55

    A. +   B. -   C. ÷

3. $900 + b = 1012$

    $b = $ _____

4. List the first three numbers using this pattern rule.

    start at 23   x 2 - 10

5. What is the rule for the following pattern:

    500, 50, 5, 0.5, 0.05, 0.005

Tuesday — Number Sense

1. Subtract:

    $789.50 - $12.99

2. What is the place value of the number in **bold**?

    58 **4**59

3. What is the difference between 9.4 and 3.7?

4. What is 482 937 in expanded form?

5. What is the greatest common factor of 18 and 72?

Wednesday | Geometry

1. What is the name of this 3D figure?

2. Which of these shapes could never have perpendicular lines?

   A. circle   B. square   C. rectangle

3. Draw an obtuse angle.

4. Calculate the measure of the missing angle.

   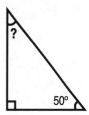

5. How many lines of symmetry does this letter have?

   # G

Thursday | Measurement

1. What is the perimeter of a heptagon with 8 m sides?

2. What would the temperature be if it were snowing?

   A. -2°C   B. 9°C   C.19°C

3. 55.9 cm = _____ m

4. What unit of measurement would you use to find a person's body mass?

   A. kg   B. L   C. km

5. How many minutes are in 4 hours and 16 minutes?

© Chalkboard Publishing

Here is a circle graph that shows how students get to school. Use the information to answer the questions.

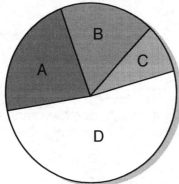

A - Drive 21%

B - Walk 18%

C - Bike 9%

D - Take the bus 52%

1. If the school has 90 students, how many students walk to school?

2. What fraction of the students drive to school?

3. What fraction of the students take the bus?

4. What percentage of students either walk or drive to school?

5. What is the most popular way to get to school?

BRAIN STRETCH

A bus travels at 80 km/hr.

1) How far will it go in 5 hours?

2) How far will it go in 10 hours?

Monday — Patterning and Algebra

1. Extend the following pattern:

   10, 19, 37, 73, ____, ____, ____

2. What is the rule for the following pattern?

   1, 4, 19, 94, 469, 2344

3. List the first three numbers in this pattern:

   start at 454, subtract 10

4. $96 + n = 123$

   n = _____

5. Is this a growing, shrinking or repeating pattern?

   75, 100, 125, 150, 175

Tuesday — Number Sense

1. Compare using: < > or =

   0.7 _____ 0.53

2. Add: $45.99 + $34.89

3. Write 128 400 in words.

4. Which number is prime?

   A. 908   B. 40   C. 11

5. Complete the equivalent fraction.

   $\dfrac{7}{9} = \dfrac{}{72}$

Wednesday Geometry

1. Why is a rectangle called a quadrilateral?

2. Calculate the measure of the missing angle.

3. Draw a 90 degree angle.

4. What is the name of this 3D figure?

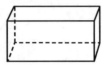

5. Which 3D figure doesn't have a curved surface?

   A. cylinder   B. cone   C. triangular prism

Thursday Measurement

1. How many months in 7 years?

2. 37 cl = _____ ml

3. Calculate the area of this triangle.

   7m

     4m

  ←——— 14 m ———→

4. 370 m=_____ km

5. What unit of measurement would you use to find the height of a ferris wheel?

Use the information from the pictograph to answer the questions.

Number of Books Read

Spencer	◇◇◇◇◇◇
Ben	◇◇◇◇◇◇◇
Madelyn	◇◇◇◇◇
Megan	◇◇◇◇◇◇
Michael	◇◇◇◇◇
Kaitlyn	◇◇◇◇◇◇◇◇◇

 = 4 books

1. How many books were read altogether? _____

2. Who read the most books? _____

3. Which two people read the same number of books? _____

4. How many books did Michael and Ben read together? _____

5. How many more books did Kaitlyn read than Spencer? _____

BRAIN STRETCH

What is the better buy? Show your work.

1. $300 for 20 books

2. $36 for 4 books

Monday — Patterning and Algebra

1. What is the rule for the following pattern:

   78, 778, 7778, 77778

2. What number is missing from the following sequence?

   18, 29, 40, 51, _____, 73

3. What will be the 8th number in this pattern?

   3, 30, 300, 3000, 30000

4. List the first three numbers for this pattern rule.

   start at 20, x 2 + 3

5. Simplify this expression using the order of operations.

   2 x 35 + 55 - 14

Tuesday — Number Sense

1. Write 77.01 in expanded form.

2. Add:

   3.456 + 4.51

3. Write this fraction in its simplest form.

   $\frac{9}{12} =$

4. Multiply:

   $\begin{array}{r} 527 \\ \times\ 283 \end{array}$

5. Change the mixed number to an improper fraction.

   $3\frac{2}{5} =$

32

© Chalkboard Publishing

Week 10

Wednesday | Geometry

1. Reflect this shape.

2. How many right angles can a triangle have?

3. If a triangle has a 20 degree angle and a 40 degree angle, what is the third angle?

4. How many lines of symmetry does this letter have?

H

5. How many vertices does a hexagon have?

Thursday | Measurement

1. What unit of measurement would you use to find the width of your thumb?

2. What are the dimensions of a square with an area of $81m^2$?

3. How many years in a millennium?

4. How much time has elapsed in between 22:05:00 and 1:25:15?

5. What is the perimeter of this figure?

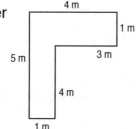

Friday   Data Management

Here is a circle graph that shows students' favourite season. Use the information to answer the questions.

Students' Favourite Season

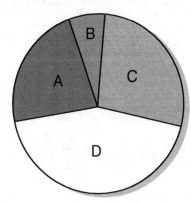

A - Spring   21%

B - Fall   9%

C - Winter   25%

D - Summer 45%

1. If the school has 80 students, how many students liked fall the best?

2. What fraction of the students liked winter?

3. What fraction of the students liked summer?

4. What percentage of students chose either spring or fall?

5. What is the most popular season?

BRAIN STRETCH

1. $22.7 \div 100 =$

2. $1.4 \div 100 =$

3. $86.5 \div 10 =$

4. $37.1 \div 10 =$

5. $572.2 \div 100 =$

6. $841.2 \div 100 =$

Monday | Patterning and Algebra

1. $100 \times n = 1200$

   $n =$ ____

2. List the first three numbers using this pattern rule.

   start at 10, x3, - 15

3. What should replace the _____ to make the following equation true?

   $6 \times 11 = 100$ _____ 34

   A. +   B. -   C. ÷

4. Is this a growing, shrinking or repeating pattern?

   102, 99, 96, 93, 90

5. Extend the following pattern:

   81, 72, 63, 54, _____, _____, _____

Tuesday | Number Sense

1. Subtract:

   45.669 - 4.390

2. Turn this improper fraction into a mixed number:

   $\dfrac{23}{4}$

3. Round this number to the nearest tenth.

   45 789.64

4. Which quotient is even?

   A. $49 \div 7$ B. $80 \div 8$ C. $18 \div 6$

5. Multiply:

   745
   x 34

Wednesday Geometry

1. Name a polygon that has less than 4 vertices.

2. Classify this angle as acute, obtuse, straight, or right.

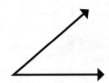

3. How many lines of symmetry does this letter have?

   M

4. What do the interior angles of a triangle equal?

5. How many edges does a cone have?

Thursday Measurement

1. 2.99 dm = _____mm

2. What is the area of the rectangle below?

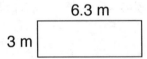

3 m   6.3 m

3. What unit of measurement would you use to find the mass of a bicycle?

4. How many decades are there in 40 years?

5. A rectangle has an area of 81 cm^2. The width is 9 cm. What is the length?

Pop Tabs Collected

	Week 1	Week 2	Week 3
Monday	23	20	13
Tuesday	11	24	6
Wednesday	30	8	13
Thursday	18	17	28
Friday	11	15	8

1. What was the total number of pop tabs collected in week 1?

2. How many more pop tabs were collected on the Mondays than on the Tuesdays?

3. What was the mode of the number of pop tabs collected in week 3?

4. What was the mean of the number of pop tabs collected in Week 2?

BRAIN STRETCH

June has 30 days. It rained on 25 of those days.

1. What was the fraction of days in June that were rainy?

2. What was the percentage of days in June that were <u>not</u> rainy?

Monday — Patterning and Algebra

1. What will be the 7th number in this pattern?

   9000, 900, 90, 9, 0.9

2. $690 \div a = 6.9$

   $a =$ _____

3. Extend the following pattern:

   250, 235, 220, 205, _____, _____, _____

4. What should replace the _____ to make the following equation true?

   $16 + 64 = 8$ _____ 10

   A. x   B. ÷   C. -

5. Ben runs 8 km every day. How many km will Ben run in 25 days?

Tuesday — Number Sense

1. How many dimes in 12 toonies?

2. Add:

   $\dfrac{1}{2} + \dfrac{2}{6} =$

3. What is the greatest possible number using the following digits?

   8 2 5 1 9

4. Write as a decimal:

   three tenths

5. Simplify the following expression using the proper order of operations.

   $71 + 41 - 3 \times 4$

Wednesday Geometry

1. What are the angles of an equilateral triangle?

2. What is an angle of 120° called?

   A. obtuse   B. right   C. acute

3. What 3D figure could be made from these pieces?

   A. cylinder
   B. rectangular prism
   C. pyramid

   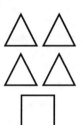

4. How many lines of symmetry does this letter have?

   Z

5. How many vertices does a rectangular prism have?

Thursday Measurement

1. The time is 11:32 am. What time will it be in 85 minutes?

2. How many decades in 4 centuries?

3. Find the perimeter of the trapezoid.

   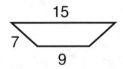

4. Calculate the area of the parallelogram.

   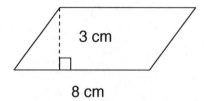

   3 cm

   8 cm

5. 73.1 km = _____ m

Complete the chart.

Set of Data	Mean	Range	Median	Mode
1. 20, 11, 20, 12, and 18				
2. 3, 17, 6, 17, 19, and 16				
3. 23, 21, 21, 20, and 18				
4. 3, 2, 5, 5, and 5				
5. 10, 10, 25, 10, and 10				

BRAIN STRETCH

If an orange tree usually bears about 65 oranges, approximately how many orange trees must a farmer have to harvest 10 000 oranges?

Patterning and Algebra

1. What will be the 19th shape in this pattern?

2. Is this a growing, shrinking or repeating pattern?

   99, 88, 77, 99, 88, 77

3. Sherri gave away a quarter of her 1896 sticker collection. How many stickers does she have left?

4. Write the first three numbers for this pattern rule:

   start at 10, double the number

5. $1.12 \times n = 11.2$

   $n = \_\_\_$

Tuesday **Number Sense**

1. Write the following as a fraction.

   0.09

2. Write the following as a decimal.

   $\dfrac{54}{100}$

3. Multiply: 34.5×8

4. Divide:

   $16\overline{)1270}$

5. Simplify the following expression using the order of the operations.

   $60 \div 4 + 18 \times 1 \times 20$

Wednesday Geometry

1. If a triangle has two angles that are 40 degrees, what kind of triangle is it?

2. How many lines of symmetry? does this letter have?

3. Find the volume of this box.

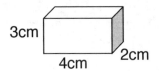

3cm
4cm
2cm

4. How many edges does this pyramid have?

5. Look at the shapes. Name the transformation.

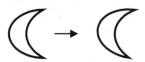

Thursday Measurement

1. 18.5 dm = _____cm

2. If a circle has a diameter of 6 cm, what is the radius?

3. Each side of a square measures 8 cm. What would the perimeter be if the sides were to increase by 3 cm?

4. What time is 15:00 on the 12 hour clock?

5. How many decades in 6 centuries?

Here are the results of a Favourite Sports Survey. Football got 15 votes, baseball 25, basketball 20, and hockey 30.

1. Create a tally chart to show the information.

Football	Baseball	Basketball	Hockey

1. How many students voted altogether? _____

2. List the results from least to greatest.

    _____

3. How many students voted for either hockey or baseball?

4. What was the most popular sport? _____

5. What was the least popular sport? _____

BRAIN STRETCH

The cookie factory produces 4630 cookies a day. If the cookies are put in boxes of 24, how many boxes are needed? Round to the nearest whole number.

Monday — Patterning and Algebra

1. 77 - 11 = 3 x _____

2. 9 x _____ = 50 - 23

3. What number is missing from the following sequence?

    11, 22, 33, 44, _____, 66

4. What is the pattern rule?

    5, 8, 11, 14, 17, 20

5. Write the first three numbers for this pattern rule:

    start at 90, subtract 4

Tuesday — Number Sense

1. How many eggs in 3 ½ dozen?

2. Order these numbers from least to greatest.

    1.01, 0.11, 1.10, 0.01

3. What is this expanded number in standard form?

    80 000 + 7000 + 400 + 80 + 1

4. What number is six thousand less than 129 904?

5. What is the lowest common multiple for 6 and 12?

Wednesday Geometry

1. Classify this angle.

2. How many lines of symmetry?

3. What 3D figure does this object look like?

4. Calculate the area of the parallelogram.

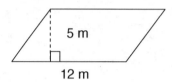

5 m

12 m

5. How many vertices does a quadrilateral have?

Thursday Measurement

1. 6m = ___mm

2. What time is 20:00 on the 12 hour clock?

3. What is the area in square metres of a pool 14 m X 20 m?

4. What time is it?

____ : ____

5. Find the perimeter of regular pentagon that has 5 cm sides.

Sort factors into the Venn Diagram, using the rules listed below.

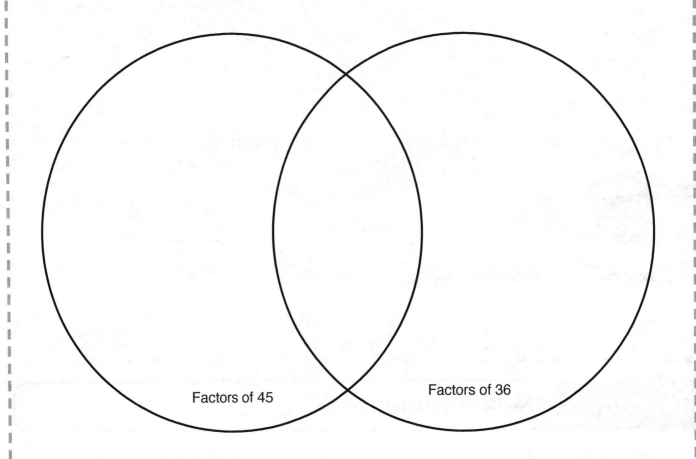

Factors of 45

Factors of 36

BRAIN STRETCH

A tin of Purrfect Cat Food is on sale for 25% off.

1) If its regular price is $3.20, what is the sale price?

2) How many cans can you buy for $5.00?

© Chalkboard Publishing

1. $7 \times n = 40 + 16$

   $n =$ _____

2. Complete this table:

b	$b \times 8$
1	
2	
3	
4	
5	

3. What is the pattern rule?

   30, 60, 90, 120, 150

4. Fill in the missing number.

   6, 24, 96, _____

5. What will be the 12th shape in this pattern?

♡ ◇ ☺ ♡

---

1. Subtract:

$$
\begin{array}{r}
300.53 \\
-\ 199.30 \\
\hline
\end{array}
$$

2. Which two numbers are both factors of 36?

   A. 9, 6   B. 6, 11   C. 4, 15

3. Ben is 25th in line. How many people are in front of him?

4. David ate 80 blueberries in an hour. How many did he eat in fifteen minutes?

5. Simplify the expression using the order of operations.

   $(8 + 1) \times (5 \times 5 - 1)$

Wednesday Geometry

1. Name a 3D figure that does _not_ have any edges.

2. How many lines of symmetry does this letter have?

3. Which figure shows a line of symmetry?

A.   B.   C.

4. What are the angles of an equilateral triangle?

5. Classify the following pair of lines.

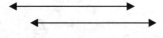

Thursday Measurement

1. What unit of measure is best to measure the distance between two cities?

2. How many metres in 36 km?

3. What is the formula for the area of a triangle?

4. A rectangle has an area of 96 cm^2. The width is 12 cm. What is the length?

4. If a car is traveling 90km/hour, how far will it go in 2.5 hours?

Week 15

Tenzin's class surveyed his schoolmates to see what their favourite ice cream flavours were. Here are his results:

12 vanilla   **20 chocolate**   **6 strawberry**   **2 bubble gum**

Fill in this pictograph using the scale of = 2 people.

Flavour	Number of People

1.   What is the range of the data?_____

2.   What is the mean?_____

3.   What is the most popular flavour?_____

4.   What is the least popular flavour?_____

BRAIN STRETCH

Sophie bought 3 T-shirts. Each T-shirt cost $22.50. How much did the T-shirts cost altogether? She paid with a $50 bill. Did she get change? Explain.

Monday   Patterning and Algebra

1. Complete the following:

   395, 399, 403, 407, _____, _____, _____

2. 7 X _____ = 84

3. What will be the 18th shape in this pattern?:

4. Each spider has 8 legs. How many legs do 15 spiders have?

5. $45 \div$ _____ $= 9$

Tuesday   Number Sense

1. Name a prime number between 10 and 20.

2. Add: 489.12 + 0.999

3. Multiply:

   $$\begin{array}{r} 0.06 \\ \times\ 0.02 \\ \hline \end{array}$$

4. Divide:

   $22)\overline{4444}$

5. List the integers in order from least to greatest.

   -11, 15, 9, -6, -10, 14

Wednesday Geometry

1. How are a square and a rectangle the same?

2. How many triangular faces does a tetrahedron have?

3. How many of the following pairs of lines intersect?

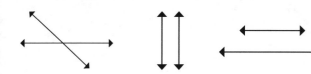

4. Classify the angle.

5. What is the size in degrees of the remaining angle if a triangle has angles of 60° and 90°?

Thursday Measurement

1. 4000 m = _____ km

2. State the best unit measure to measure a drop of rain.

3. What time is 8:00 pm in 24 hour notation?

4. The time is 9:14 a.m. What time will it be in 79 minutes?

5. Find the perimeter of an octagon if all of the sides equal 9 m.

© Chalkboard Publishing

Jordan is creating a board game to play with is brothers. He wants to design a spinner that is has these probabilities.

¼ green , ⅛ orange, ⅛ red, ⅜ blue, ⅛ purple

Please design a spinner for Jordan in the space below.

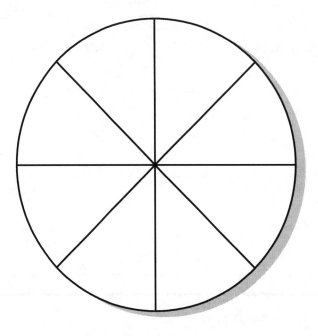

1. Which colour is the spinner most likely to land on? _____

2. Which colours have a 1/8 chance of being spun? _____

3. Which colour has the greatest chance of being spun? _____

4. Which colours have the least chance of being spun? _____

BRAIN STRETCH

If 72 chicken dinners cost $695, how much does 1 chicken dinner cost?
Round your answer to the nearest penny.

Monday — Patterning and Algebra

1. Divide: 78.8 by 4

2. Put the following numbers in order from least to greatest:

   5.22, 5.5, 5.6, 5.1

3. Multiply:

   $$\begin{array}{r} 0.598 \\ \times\ \ 4.200 \\ \hline \end{array}$$

4. Complete this table:

x	X + 14
1	
2	
3	
4	
5	

5. Simplify the expression using the order of operations.

   (973 - 465) - (5 + 53) + 394

Tuesday — Number Sense

1. What is the next number if the pattern rule is "subtract 60"?

   120, _____

2. Fill in the missing number.

   999, 959, 919, _____

3. There were 234 people who attended a hockey game. If each ticket cost $11.00 how much money was collected?

4. What is the least possible number using the following digits?

   4 2 5 1 9

5. In which number sentence does a 4 make the equation true?

   A. 4 x _____ = 32   B. 16 ÷ _____ = 4   C. 24 + _____ = 30

Wednesday Geometry

1. How many lines of symmetry does a pentagon have?

2. Which of these is an acute angle?

   A. 4°   B. 140°   C. 185°

3. Draw an obtuse angle.

4. Define a straight angle.

5. Which pair of shapes look congruent?

   A.   W and X   B. X and Y   C. W and Z

Thursday Measurement

1. Liam biked 25 km in 1.5 hours. How long will it take for him to bike 100km?

2. Find the perimeter of an octagon with 3 cm sides.

3. What unit of measure would you use to measure the capacity of a juice carton?

4. Find the surface area of the figure.

6 m

8 m

11 m

5. What is the area of the circle? Round to the nearest hundreth.

   Assume π = 3.14.

   m = 32 cm

The town of Melrose kept a record of its rainfall for six months. Here are the results:

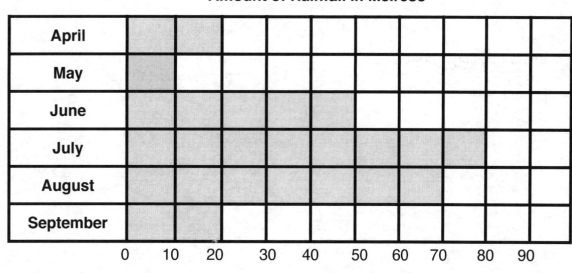

Amount of Rainfall in Melrose

MONTH		0	10	20	30	40	50	60	70	80	90
	April										
	May										
	June										
	July										
	August										
	September										

Amount of rainfall in mm

1. Which months had more than 40 mm of rainfall? _____

2. Which month had the most rainfall? _____

3. How much rain fall was there altogether? _____

BRAIN STRETCH

Chris wanted to buy some soda pop for a party. He had a choice of buying a case of 24 cans of soda pop or 4 six-packs. One case of 24 soda pop cans costs $8.44. A six-pack of soda pop cans costs $2.95. Which is the better buy?

Monday   Patterning and Algebra

1. What is the pattern rule?

   10, 23, 49, 101, 205

2. What kind of pattern is the pattern in question #1?

3. Fill in the missing number.

   1, 3, 7, 15, ___, 63

4. Complete by evaluating the expression.

   $6d$
   for $d = 6$

5. What is the missing number?

   11 X ____ = 176

Tuesday   Number Sense

1. Michael spent $1.55 on an ice cream cone and $0.95 on a soda. How much change will he get back from a five dollar bill?

2. Which of the following numbers is composite?

   4,   5,   9,   15

3. There are 20 cookies eaten out of a box of 40. What percent of the cookies has been eaten?

4. Write the following in decimal form.

   ten and nineteen hundredths

5. Multiply:

   56.41 X 1000 =

Wednesday Geometry

1. Classify the angle.

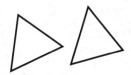

2. Is this an equilateral triangle?

3. Which 3D figure has no faces?

   A. triangular prism
   B. sphere
   C. cone
   D. cylinder

4. Calculate the measure of the missing angle.

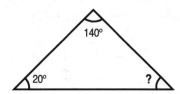

5. Are these shapes congruent or similar?

Thursday Measurement

1. How are the area of a parallelogram and the area of a rectangle related?

2. 5.6 m = _____ dm

3. 3 years = ___ weeks?

4. Chris got home from baseball practice at 5:30 pm. What time is that in 24 hour notation?

5. What is the area? Round to the nearest hundredth. Assume π = 3.14.

m = 16

Sort factors into the Venn Diagram, using the rules listed below.

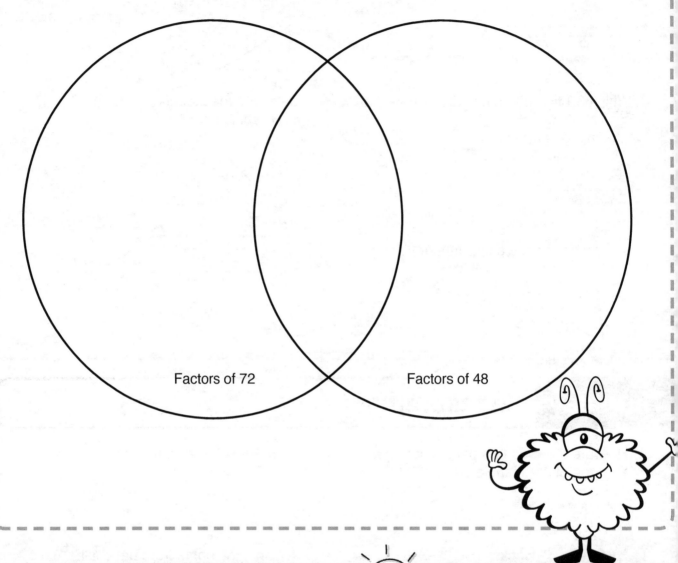

Factors of 72   Factors of 48

BRAIN STRETCH

A box of cookies weighs 420 grams. If Megan brought two boxes for the class party, what is the combined weight of both boxes of cookies in kilograms?

Monday — Patterning and Algebra

1. Complete the function table:

x	X + 25 - 5
1	
2	
3	
4	
5	

2. What are the first three numbers for this pattern rule?

   start at 880, subtract 25

3. Simplify the expression using the proper order of operations.

   $52 \div 4 + (63 \div 7 - 1)$

4. Fill in the missing number.

   5, 12, 26, _____, 110

5. Complete by evaluating the expression.

   $5g$
   for $g = 9$

Tuesday — Number Sense

1. List the integers in order from least to greatest.

   -30, -24, 17, 47

2. Change the mixed number to an improper fraction.

   $3\frac{4}{7} =$

3. Divide:

   $3\overline{)93.6}$

4. In a class of 30, 18 students are girls. What is the ratio of girls to boys?

5. A bunch of flowers costs $8.99. How much will 5 bunches cost?

1. Look at the shapes. Name the transformation.

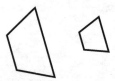

3. Are these shapes congruent or similar?

5. Which of these are parallelograms?

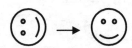

A. shapes B & A   B. shapes D& C   C. shapes B &D

3. How many lines of symmetry?

B

4. Which figure has more than 5 sides?

A. trapezoid

B. pentagon

C. hexagon

Thursday   Measurement

1. What is the radius of a circle whose diameter is 64 cm?

2. How many decades in 6 centuries?

3. Find the area of this shape:

12 cm

16 cm

4. 0.4 km = _____ dm

5. If the average speed of a motorist is 50 km per hour, calculate the distance if he or she travelled for 2 hours.

Find the mean for each set of data on these stem and leaf plots.

1.

Stem	Leaves
15	1
16	1 2
17	4

2.

Stem	Leaves
1	3 5 6 7
2	3 8
3	0 0 2 6

BRAIN STRETCH

David ran 100 metres in 51 seconds. Paul ran 1 kilometre in 5 minutes 12 seconds.
Who was the faster runner? Explain your thinking.

Monday | Patterning and Algebra

1. Complete by evaluating the expression.

   $8e + 5$
   for $e = 3$

2. Complete the function table.

x	2x +2
1	
2	
3	
4	
5	

3. What will be the 3rd number for this pattern rule?

   start at 4, multiply by 3

4. Create a repeating pattern.

5. Fill in the missing number.

   100, 300, 900, _____, 8100

Tuesday | Number Sense

1. If you cut a cake into slices, choose which fraction shows the slice of cake that is the smallest piece.

   A. $\frac{1}{4}$ B. $\frac{1}{2}$ C. $\frac{3}{4}$

2. 8 is not a factor of:

   A. 48   B. 24   C. 52

3. Kaitlyn bought three notebooks at $2.35 each. How much did she spend in total?

4. Subtract:

   $25.6 - 12.07$

5. Write the following as a numeral.

   nine hundred eighteen thousand fifty-five

Week 20

Wednesday Geometry

1. How many vertices does a hexagonal prism have?

2. Are the shapes congruent or similar?

3. Classify this angle.

4. If the angles of a triangle measure 50°, 65° and 65°, what type of triangle is it?

5. How many edges does a cube have?

Thursday Measurement

1. What unit would you use to measure the mass of a vitamin tablet?

   A. mg   B. mm   C. ml

2. What time is 14:24 on a 12 hour clock?

3. What is the year 2 decades after 1969?

4. 0.5 km = _____ mm

4. If Mario drives 725 km to Montreal at a speed of 100 km per hour, how long will it take him to get there?

© Chalkboard Publishing

Find the mean for each set of data.

1.

Stem	Leaves
33	1 2 7 8
34	1 5 5 5 6
17	4

2.

Stem	Leaves
11	7
12	1 5 8
13	0
14	
15	4 4 9

BRAIN STRETCH

Sophie made a round picture frame that is 20 cm in diameter. She wants to wrap a blue ribbon around the outside of the frame two times and needs to know how long the ribbon should be. How long should the ribbon be?

© Chalkboard Publishing

Monday — Patterning and Algebra

1. Fill in the missing number.

   1, 4, 9, 16, ___. 36

2. Complete by evaluating the expression.

   $9d + 4$
   for $d = 2$

3. Complete this function table:

x	36 - x
1	
2	
3	
4	
5	

4. Solve the equation.

   $42 \div n = 6$

5. What is the missing number?

   $144 \div$ ____ $= 12$

Tuesday — Number Sense

1. Mr. Bruce gave out six prize pencils each week day. How many does he give away in nine weeks?

2. Divide: 60.5 by 5

3. Write 49 156 in words.

4. Jake's grandfather is 84 years old. What is his age in months?

5. Add:

   54 678 + 19 431 =

Wednesday | Geometry

1. What 3D figure does this object look like?

   A. cone

   B. sphere

   C. cylinder

2. Classify the following group of lines:

3. How many lines of symmetry?

   P

4. Which 3D figure has 8 edges?

   A.   B.   C.

   D. none

5. Which 3D figure has 12 edges?

Thursday | Measurement

1. Write the time difference.

   from 08:32 to 12:41

2. What tool would you use to measure the temperature?

3. How many centuries in 1200 years?

4. Calculate the volume.

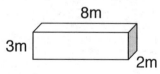

   8m

   3m

   2m

5. 650 mm = _____ cm

Mrs. Turnbull felt that a stop sign should be placed on the street in front of her house to stop cars from speeding down the road. She asked her daughter Madelyn to survey the number of cars that drove past their home every day for an hour after school. She created a pictograph to show her results.

Day	Number of Cars
Monday	🚗 🚗 🚗
Tuesday	🚗 🚗 🚗 🚗
Wednesday	🚗 🚗 🚗 🚗 🚗
Thursday	🚗 🚗 🚗 🚗
Friday	🚗 🚗 🚗

🚗 = 10 cars

1. What day did the most cars travel past Madelyn's house? _____

2. What day did the least number of cars pass her house?_____

3. How many cars did Madelyn count altogether?_____

4. What day did 50 cars pass her house? _____

5. What was the range number of cars that passed her house each day after school?_____

BRAIN STRETCH

Ross has twenty-one hammers in his toolbox. Two-thirds of them are broken. How many hammers are broken?

Monday — Patterning and Algebra

1. Simplify the expression using the proper order of operations.

   (89.52 + 3 + 24.33) - 5.7

2. Fill in the missing number.

   100, 121, 144, _____, 196

3. What is the missing number?

   180 X _____ = 0.18

4. What is the twentieth shape in this pattern?

5. Create a shrinking pattern.

Tuesday — Number Sense

1. What is the value of 7 in the number 19 734?

   A. 70 000

   B. 7000

   C. 700

2. What is 1789 rounded to the nearest thousand?

3. Daniel buys 1:4 apples to oranges. If he bought 10 apples, how many oranges did he buy?

4. Choose: >, <, or =

   0.08 ☐ 1.08

5. What is the lowest common multiple of 2 and 10?

Wednesday | Geometry

1. How many lines of symmetry does this number have?

9

2. What are 4 sided figures called?

3. How many edges does rectangular prism have?

4. Classify this angle.

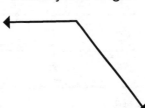

5. Name a quadrilateral that has two pairs of 90 degree angles?

Thursday | Measurement

1. 1.2 km = _____ dm

2. Write the time difference.

   from 08:45 to 16:20

3. What object is shorter in length than a decimetre?

   A. an ant   B. a bus   C. a metre stick

4. What year is 3 decades before 1969?

5. What is the best estimate for the mass of two books?

   A. 1 kg   B. 1 g   C. 1000 kg

Mrs. Stephenson kept a gardener's journal to track the growth of her geranium plants. Here is the data she collected in July and August.

Plant	July	August
#1	10 cm	14 cm
#2	9 cm	11 cm
#3	12 cm	13 cm
#4	12 cm	15 cm
#5	11 cm	12 cm
#6	14 cm	17 cm
#7	8 cm	11 cm

1. What is the range of the data in July? _____

2. What is the mean height of the plants in July? _____

3. What is the range of the data in August? _____

4. What is the mean height of the plants in August? _____

5. What is the difference between the mean heights? _____

BRAIN STRETCH

Katherine has forty-two dresses. One-sixth of her dresses are blue. How many of Katherine's dresses are blue?

Monday   Patterning and Algebra

1. Fill in the missing number.

   50, 102, 206, ___, 830

2. Complete by evaluating the expression.

   $5d + 8$
   for $d = 3$

3. Which division fact has the same quotient as $48 \div 8$?

   A. $32 \div 4$ B. $48 \div 8$ C. $27 \div 3$

4. Solve the equation.

   $4 \times p = 56$

5. Create a repeating pattern using:

Tuesday   Number Sense

1. Which even numbers are between 50 and 70 and are a multiple of six?

2. Divide:

   $19\overline{)76}$

3. Write the numeral in expanded form.

   569 831

4. How many of the following numbers are odd?

   15, 76, 23, 91, 40

   A. 3   B. 4   C. 5

4. Write as a decimal number.

   $\dfrac{40}{50}$

Wednesday Geometry

1. Calculate the measure of the missing angle.

60°
105°
?

2. Name two 3D shapes that can roll.

3. Flip this shape over the line.

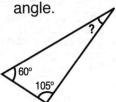

4. What shape is the face of a hexagonal prism?

5. Which 3D figure does this object look like?

Thursday Measurement

1. What is the best estimate for the capacity of a cup of hot chocolate?

   A. 200 l   B. 200 ml   C. 2 ml

2. A rectangle is 9 cm long and 7cm wide. What is the perimeter if the length decreased by 2 cm?

3. 17.8 cm = _____m

4. Write the time difference.

   from 16:13 to 23:21

5. Calculate the area of the parallelogram.

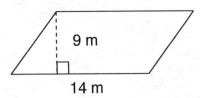

9 m

14 m

© Chalkboard Publishing

Week 23

Spencer had a bag of marbles. In his bag he had:

8 black marbles	18 red marbles
19 orange marbles	13 blue marbles

1. State the ratio of orange marbles to all the marbles.

2. State the ratio of blue marbles to all the marbles.

3. State the ratio of black marbles to orange and blue marbles.

4. State the ratio of red marbles to black marbles.

BRAIN STRETCH

If Baycrest Car Dealership sells 5 silver cars for every 2 red ones, how many silver cars did they sell last year if they sold 50 red cars?

1. Fill in the missing number.

   100, 125, 150, _____, 200

2. Complete by evaluating the expression.

   $6d - 4$
   for $d = 4$

3. Which multiplication fact has the same product as   8 X 5?

   A. 10 X 4   B. 7 X 6   C. 9 X 4

4. Solve the equation.

   $4 \times p = 36$

5. Create a repeating pattern using numbers:

1. Ben reads one comic book for every 5 novels. How many comics did Ben read if he read 20 novels?

2. Write the numeral 802 300 in words.

3. Subtract:

   775.25 – 30.12

4. What are the prime numbers between 30 and 35?

5. Write the decimal as a fraction.

   0.08

Wednesday | Geometry

1. What makes two figures congruent?

2. What makes two figures similar?

3. What 3D figure does this object look like?

4. How many lines of symmetry?

G

5. How many of the following pairs of lines are parallel?

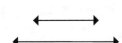

A. 1
B. 2
C. 3

Thursday | Measurement

1. If you are traveling 50 km per hour. How long would it take you to go 725 km?

2. 50 km = _____ cm

3. What is the area in square metres of a pool 16m X 18 m?

4. Find the perimeter of the octagon.

7

5. Calculate the area of the parallelogram.

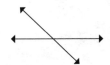

1.2 m

3 m

Here is a double bar graph of how much money two classes collected for a class trip.

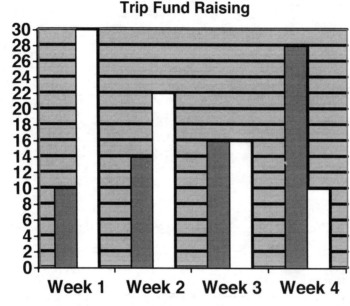

Trip Fund Raising

Amount of money raised in $

Class A
Class B

Week 1   Week 2   Week 3   Week 4

1. Which class raised the most money? _____

2. How much money did class A raise in weeks 3 and 4? _____

3. In what week did both classes raise the same amount of money? _____

4. How much money did class B raise in weeks 1 and 2? _____

BRAIN STRETCH

Two hundred sixty five people visited the circus on Tuesday, three hundred ninety-nine on Wednesday, and three hundred forty-one on Thursday. How many people visited the circus from Tuesday to Thursday?

Monday   Patterning and Algebra

1. What should replace the _____ to make the following equation true?

    8 X 3 = 99 _____ 75

    A.   +   B.   -   C.   ÷

2. Create a repeating pattern.

3. What number comes next?

    774, 764, 754, _____

4. Complete the function table:

x	6x-1
1	
2	
3	
4	
5	

5. Indicate the value of b.

    b X 5 + 12 = 47

Tuesday   Number Sense

1. Write the improper fraction as a mixed number.

    $\frac{35}{2}$

2. Add:

    $$\begin{array}{r} 475 \\ 591 \\ + \underline{284} \end{array}$$

3. Write four hundred twenty-two dollars and nineteen cents in numerals.

4. Subtract:

    $$\begin{array}{r} 79\ 805 \\ - \underline{35\ 752} \end{array}$$

5. What is the greatest common factor for 32 and 40?

Wednesday Geometry

1. Draw a pair of congruent figures.

2. How many lines of symmetry?

2. How many degrees are there in a circle?

4. What is an angle that is 45° called?

   A. right   B. acute   C. straight   D. obtuse

5. What 3D figure could be made from these pieces?

   A. cylinder   B. rectangular prism   C. pyramid

Thursday Measurement

1. How many minutes in 12 hours?

2. What is the area of this parallelogram?

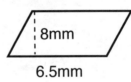

   8mm

   6.5mm

3. 6.50 km = _____ cm

4. 36500 days = _____ years

5. If you travel 78km in three hours, how fast are you traveling?

© Chalkboard Publishing

Donald's basketball team measured the height of each player and surveyed their shoe size to see if there was a relationship between the two measurements. Here are the results:

Player	Height	Shoe Size
Chris	190 cm	10
Mario	194 cm	10.5
Liam	180 cm	9
Deepak	182 cm	9.5
Steven	201 cm	11.5
Shawn	198 cm	11
Michael	202 cm	12
George	181 cm	10
Ben	175 cm	9
Spencer	180 cm	10
David	183 cm	10

1.　What is the mean shoe size?_____

2.　What is the mode shoe size?_____

3.　What is the median shoe size?_____

4.　What is the mean height of the players?_____

5.　Is there a relationship between height and shoe size? Explain.

　　_____

BRAIN STRETCH

What is the better buy?

　　　A. 8 DVDs for $88　　　　　　B. 21 DVDs for $168

Monday | Patterning and Algebra

1. What should replace the _____ to make the following equation true?

   $18 \div 3 = 42$ _____ 7

   A. +   B. -   C. $\div$

2. Predict what the 16th animal will be in this pattern.

   A.    B.   C.

3. What number comes next?

   989, 979, 969, _____

4. Create a shrinking pattern.

5. Calculate the value of b.

   $b \times 5 - 10 = 90$

Tuesday | Number Sense

1. What is 25% of 100

2. Multiply:

   $$\begin{array}{r} 987 \\ \times\ 34 \\ \hline \end{array}$$

3. What are the prime numbers between 15 and 25?

4. Multiply:

   59.41×1000

5. Simplify the expression using the order of operations.

   $(4 + 8) - (70 - 65)$

1. How are a triangle and a hexagon different?

2. How many lines of symmetry does this letter have?

3. Name the transformation. Choose reflection, translation or rotation

4. How many faces does a cylinder have?

5. Name the transformation. Choose reflection, translation or rotation.

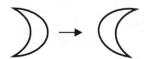

Thursday **Measurement**

1. What is the surface area of this prism?

11 m
2 m
10 m

2. 0.02 l = _____ ml

3. 375.3 cm =_____m

4. What is the volume of the shape in question 1?

5. Which shape has 2 pairs of parallel sides, and 2 pairs of angles that are equal?

A. △   B. ▱   C. ⬯

Friday   Data Management

Complete the chart.

Set of Data	Mean	Range	Mode
1. 29, 29, 20, 4, and 28			
2. 13, 12, 6, 7, and 7			
3. 14, 17, 8, 14, and 2			
4. 7, 17, 17, 12, and 17			
5. 14, 18, 17, 18, and 18			

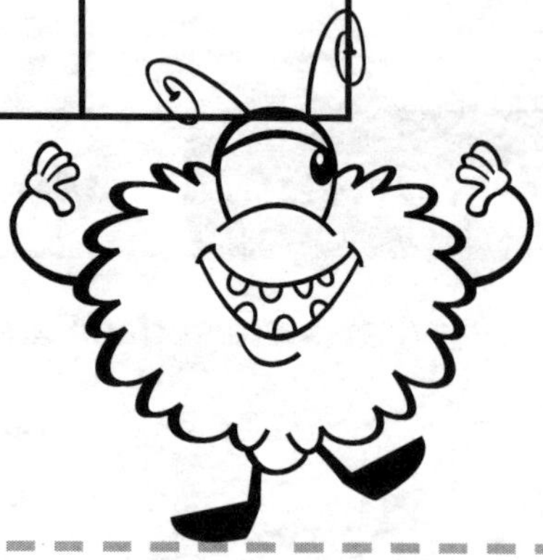

BRAIN STRETCH

What is a better buy?

A. 11 pens for $2.64

B. 31 pens for $8.36

1. Find r.

   If $r - 6 = 22$.

2. Complete by evaluating the expression.

   $b^2 - 3b + 10$

   for $b = 12$

3. Complete the table:

x	2x + 3
1	
2	
3	
4	
5	

4. There are 12 roses in each vase. How many roses in 30 vases?

5. Create a growing pattern.

1. Simplify the expression using the proper order of operations.

   $2 \times 3 - (12 - 8)$

2. Order this set from the least to the greatest part of a unit.

   $\frac{1}{4}$ 0.07   60 %

3. Divide:

   $4\overline{)688.4}$

4. What is 30% of $270.00?

5. What is the greatest common factor for 12 and 32?

Wednesday | Geometry

1. How many lines of symmetry does this number have?

3

2. Name a quadrilateral that has four equal sides.

3. Name one way the attributes of a rhombus and a trapezoid are the same.

4. What is the measure of the missing angle?

5. Are these shapes congruent or similar?

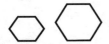

Thursday | Measurement

1. If Bill can type 24 words per minute, how many can he type in an hour?

2. Find the surface area of the figure.

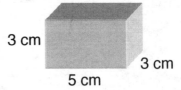

3 cm
3 cm
5 cm

3. Valerie got home from baseball practice at 9:30 pm. State the time in 24 hour notation.

4. A rectangle has an area of 84 cm^2. The width is 12 cm. What is the length?

5. How many days in 3 centuries?

Mrs. Monroe took a survey of what foods her students preferred to buy from the cafeteria. Here are the results:

	Number of Votes
French Fries	18
Hamburgers	22
Meat Patties	11
Sandwiches	15
Salads	22
Soups	8

1. What was the most popular choice? _____

2. What was the least popular choice? _____

3. What is the range of the data collected? _____

4. What is the mean? _____

5. How many students were surveyed? _____

6. How many more students chose salads than French fries? _____

BRAIN STRETCH

At Big Bob's BBQ restaurant, rectangle tables were put together to sit people. A single rectangle table seats 4 people. Two rectangle tables placed together seats 8 people. How many people can be seated if 9 tables are placed together?

Monday | Patterning and Algebra

1. What should replace the _____ to make the following equation true?

   9 x 3 = 30 _____ 3

   A. +   B. -   C. ÷

2. Predict what the 16th animal will be in this pattern.

   A.
   B.
   C.

3. What number comes next?

   1000, 900, 800, _____

4. Create a repeating pattern.

5. Indicate the value of b.

   b X 6 + 3 = 39

Tuesday | Number Sense

1. Reduce the fraction to lowest terms.

   $\frac{16}{18}$

2. Find 75% of 32.

3. Write the decimal.

   two hundredths

4. Multiply and write the answer in simplest form:

   $7 \times \frac{2}{3}$

5. What are the prime numbers between 80 and 90?

Wednesday | Geometry

1. How are the attributes of a triangle and a hexagon different?

2. How many lines of symmetry does this letter have?

3. What is the measure of the missing angle?

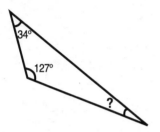

4. Name the transformation. Choose reflection, translation or rotation.

5. What is an angle of 53° called?

   A. obtuse   B. right   C. acute

Thursday | Measurement

1. What is the best estimate for the length of a worm?

   A. 3 cm   B. 3 m   C. 3 km

2. Craig lives 850 000 cm from his school. How many metres is that?

3. There are 20 g of candy in a bag. How many mg of candy are there in 2 bags?

4. It is now 12:36 pm. What time will it be in 38 minutes?7

5. A rectangle is 8 cm long and 6 cm wide. What is the perimeter if the length is decreased by 1 cm?

© Chalkboard Publishing

Answer the probability questions using the information on the two spinners.

Spinner 1

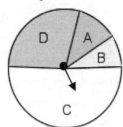

Spinner 2

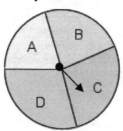

If someone has only 1 spin:

1. Is spinning C more probable on Spinner 1 or Spinner 2? _____

2. On which spinner is A more probable? _____

3. On which spinner is B less probable? _____

4. Which letter is equally likely on both Spinner 1 and Spinner 2? _____

BRAIN STRETCH

In how many ways can Stephen, Chris, and Mathew stand in line?

Monday | Patterning and Algebra

1. Ben has 30 bags of jelly beans. Each bag has 120 jelly beans. Which number sentence finds the total jelly beans Ben has?

   A. 30 x 120   B. 30 + 120   C. 120 ÷ 30

2. Predict what the 11th animal will be in this pattern.

   A.    B.   C.

3. What number comes next?

   725, 625, 525, _____

4. Complete by evaluating the expression.

   $b^2 - 3b + 10$

   for $b = 8$

5. Which number sentence has the same answer as 14 x 8?

   A. 120 − 8   B. 122 + 30   C. 100 ÷ 4

Tuesday | Number Sense

1. Divide: 925.5 by 5

2. Write as a numeral:

   three hundred seventy-three thousand twelve

3. What is 10% of 30?

4. Order this set from the least to the greatest part of a unit.

   $\frac{1}{5}$ 70%   0.03

5. Which even number is between 40 and 50 and is a multiple of six?

   A. 42   B. 46   C. 44

© Chalkboard Publishing

Wednesday | Geometry

1. What shape does this object look like?

2. How many lines of symmetry does this letter have?

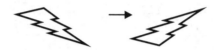

3. Are these shapes congruent, similar or neither?

4. Name the transformation. Choose reflection, translation or rotation.

5. What is an angle of 140° called?

   A. obtuse   B. right   C. acute

Thursday | Measurement

1. How many metres in 160 km?

2. 45 mg = ____g

3. A rectangle has an area of 240 cm². The width is 15 cm. What is the length?

4. Each side of a pentagon measures 8 cm. What would the perimeter be if the sides were to increase by 2 cm each?

5. The time is 7:15 p.m. What time will it be in 2 hour and 10 minutes?

Week 29

Banting Public School held their annual cookie sale. Here are the amounts of cookies sold.

Cookie	Cookies Sold
Oatmeal	198
Chocolate Chip	220
Double Chocolate	295
Vanilla Crème	165

1. List the types of cookies sold from least to greatest.

_____

2. What was the ratio of oatmeal cookies sold to vanilla crème? _____

3. How many more double chocolate cookies were sold than chocolate chip? _____

4. How many cookies were sold altogether? _____

5. If each cookie sold for $0.75, how much money was raised altogether? _____

BRAIN STRETCH

Katherine and Alexander went to the grocery store to buy 2 dozen eggs. When they opened the egg carton at home they saw that 1/4 of the eggs were broken.

1. How many eggs were broken?

2. How many eggs were not broken?

Monday — Patterning and Algebra

1. Simplify the expression using the proper order of operations.

    $3 + 2 \times 8 - 1$

2. Predict what the 15th animal will be in this pattern.

    A. 🐧   B. 🐸   C. 🐘

3. What number comes next?

    5, 25, 125, 625, _____

4. Complete by evaluating the expression.

    $11(9 + t) - 87$

    for $t = 43$

5. Which number sentence has the same answer as 5 X 5?

    A. $120 - 8$ B. $122 + 30$ C. $100 \div 4$

Tuesday — Number Sense

1. Which number comes between 4.57 and 4.74?

    A. 4.98   B. 4.63   C. 4.41

2. Which of the following numerals has a 6 in the hundredths place?

    A. 9.67   B. 6.79   C. 7.96

3. Write 6 ¾ as an improper fraction.

4. What is 25% of 200?

5. Which of the following numbers when rounded to the nearest 10 is 4230 and when rounded to the nearest 1000 is 4000?

    A. 4231   B. 3867   C. 4145

Wednesday — Geometry

1. What 3D figure does this object look like?

2. How many lines of symmetry does this letter have?

C

3. Are these shapes congruent, similar or neither?

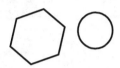

4. Name the transformation. Choose reflection, translation or rotation.

5. What is an angle of 34° called?

   A. obtuse   B. right   C. acute

Thursday — Measurement

1. 26 900 cg = _____ kg

2. David could shoot 18 baskets in one minute. How many should he be able to shoot in an hour?

3. Find the surface area of the figure.

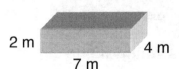

2 m   4 m
   7 m

4. An aquarium is 12 m wide, 18 m long and 5 m deep. What is its volume?

5. Calculate the perimeter.

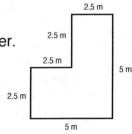

2.5 m
2.5 m
2.5 m
5 m
2.5 m
5 m

Use the information below to complete the questions.

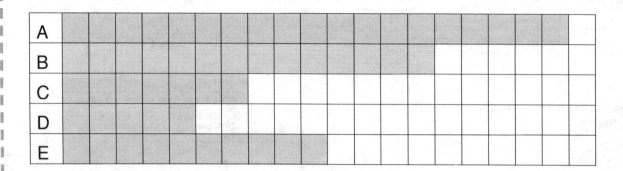

There are 20 spaces in each row:

1. Which row shows 50% of the row is filled? _____

2. Which row shows 0.25 of the row is filled? _____

3. What percent of row B is filled? _____

4. How much more of row A is filled than row D? _____

5. Which row is filled between ¼ and ½? _____

BRAIN STRETCH

When Sophie has something to drink, 2 out of 5 times it is water. If she has 50 drinks in a week, how many of them will be water?

Test 1—Multiplying by 1 to 6

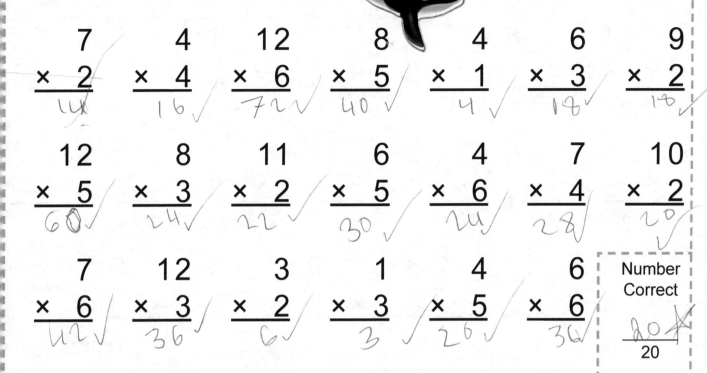

7	4	12	8	4	6	9
× 2	× 4	× 6	× 5	× 1	× 3	× 2
44	16	72	40	4	18	18

12	8	11	6	4	7	10
× 5	× 3	× 2	× 5	× 6	× 4	× 2
60	24	22	30	24	28	20

7	12	3	1	4	6
× 6	× 3	× 2	× 3	× 5	× 6
42	36	6	3	20	36

Number Correct

20 / 20

Test 2—Multiplying by 1 to 6

6	7	12	4	5	9	4
× 4	× 3	× 5	× 3	× 5	× 2	× 1
24	21	60	12	25	18	4

2	11	10	8	7	9	4
× 6	× 2	× 3	× 6	× 1	× 4	× 4
12	22	30	48	7	36	16

8	5	3	1	10	11
× 3	× 2	× 5	× 1	× 4	× 6
24	10	15	1	40	66

Number Correct

20 / 20

Test 3—Multiplying by 1 to 6

11	8	9	3	1	5	12
× 3	× 1	× 5	× 4	× 2	× 5	× 4
33	8	45	12	2	25	48

7	4	2	11	3	8	6
× 6	× 5	× 1	× 6	× 2	× 5	× 2
42	20	2	66	6	40	12

6	10	8	9	5	6
× 4	× 2	× 3	× 6	× 3	× 3
24	20	24	54	15	18

Number Correct

$\frac{20}{20}$

Test 4—Multiplying by 1 to 6

5	9	11	8	7	10	8
× 4	× 1	× 3	× 4	× 3	× 5	× 6
40	9	33	32	21	50	48

3	11	2	10	6	6	5
× 3	× 4	× 1	× 6	× 5	× 3	× 6
9	44	2	60	30	18	30

3	7	12	9	9	10
× 1	× 2	× 5	× 6	× 2	× 4
3	14	60	54	18	40

Number Correct

$\frac{}{20}$

Test 5—Multiplying by 1 to 6

7	10	1	4	12	4	3
× 2	× 6	× 2	× 5	× 3	× 4	× 4
14	66	2	20	36	16	12

9	6	3	11	10	7	5
× 5	× 4	× 5	× 2	× 3	× 6	× 6
45	24	15	22	30	42	30

12	11	2	6	8	9
× 6	× 1	× 5	× 3	× 1	× 2
72	11	10	18	8	18

Number Correct

20 / 20

Test 6—Multiplying by 1 to 6

5	3	8	8	12	1	9
× 4	× 3	× 3	× 6	× 1	× 2	× 6
20	9	24	48	12	2	54

9	4	3	5	3	8	6
× 4	× 1	× 2	× 3	× 4	× 4	× 6
36	4	6	15	12	32	36

10	6	12	11	5	2
× 4	× 5	× 6	× 5	× 1	× 5
40	30	72	55	5	10

Number Correct

20 / 20

Test 7—Multiplying by 1 to 6

7	5	7	5	10	6	6
× 3	× 2	× 6	× 6	× 5	× 4	× 2
21	16	42	30	50	24	12

8	12	2	11	1	1	9
× 5	× 4	× 5	× 3	× 3	× 1	× 2
40	48	10	33	3	1	18

6	8	2	12	4	10
× 5	× 4	× 1	× 6	× 3	× 1
30	32	2	72	17	10

Number Correct

$\dfrac{20}{20}$

Test 8—Multiplying by 1 to 6

11	5	5	1	12	10	4
× 4	× 3	× 2	× 6	× 5	× 4	× 3
44	15	10	6	60	40	17

9	4	6	4	3	3	8
× 3	× 6	× 5	× 2	× 3	× 1	× 4
27	24	30	8	9	3	32

3	10	11	8	7	3
× 4	× 2	× 6	× 5	× 3	× 2
12	20	66	40	21	6

Number Correct

$\dfrac{20}{20}$

Test 3—Multiplying by 7 to 12

9	3	5	11	10	9	3
× 11	× 10	× 10	× 8	× 12	× 9	× 7
99	36	50	88	120	81	21

11	10	6	6	7	8	12
× 11	× 7	× 12	× 8	× 7	× 8	× 9
110	70	52	48	49	64	108

12	9	8	6	2	2
× 10	× 12	× 11	× 7	× 9	× 11
120	108	80	42	18	22

Number Correct

___
20

Test 4—Multiplying by 7 to 12

7	5	9	4	11	12	2
× 12	× 8	× 10	× 9	× 7	× 11	× 8
84	40	90	36	72	132	16

3	10	5	8	4	2	1
× 10	× 8	× 12	× 9	× 10	× 7	× 10
30	80	60	72	40	14	10

9	1	3	7	6	6
× 8	× 12	× 11	× 10	× 9	× 8
72	12	33	70	54	48

Number Correct

___
20

24
+ 24
—
72

Test 5—Multiplying by 7 to 12

2	12	8	9	11	6	7
× 11	× 10	× 9	× 10	× 8	× 12	× 7
22	120	72	90	88	72	49

9	5	6	4	7	10	7
× 8	× 9	× 10	× 7	× 8	× 7	× 11
72	45	60	28			

8	3	7	12	10	10
× 11	× 12	× 9	× 7	× 12	× 10

Number Correct

———
20

Test 6—Multiplying by 7 to 12

10	4	5	1	7	12	9
× 7	× 10	× 8	× 12	× 11	× 7	× 8

5	8	12	3	11	3	7
× 11	× 10	× 9	× 8	× 10	× 12	× 9

9	6	8	4	9	6
× 11	× 12	× 8	× 9	× 7	× 7

Number Correct

———
20

Test 7—Multiplying by 7 to 12

11	7	7	10	1	6	4
× 9	× 8	× 7	× 10	× 8	× 9	× 11

6	12	5	9	3	12	9
× 8	× 9	× 12	× 10	× 8	× 10	× 7

6	8	8	5	9	8
× 7	× 9	× 12	× 7	× 11	× 10

Number Correct

___
20

Test 8—Multiplying by 7 to 12

8	8	9	3	4	11	6
× 12	× 8	× 9	× 11	× 10	× 7	× 8

7	8	10	6	1	6	4
× 7	× 10	× 9	× 11	× 7	× 12	× 9

7	5	12	10	3	7
× 10	× 12	× 7	× 11	× 8	× 9

Number Correct

___
20

Test 9—Multiplying by 7 to 12

9	7	4	8	8	10	12
× 10	× 12	× 9	× 8	× 11	× 10	× 7

1	3	6	4	5	2	9
× 10	× 11	× 8	× 12	× 7	× 8	× 9

6	2	7	11	4	10
× 11	× 7	× 8	× 12	× 10	× 9

Number Correct

___
20

Test 10—Multiplying by 7 to 12

9	9	11	9	8	10	2
× 10	× 9	× 8	× 11	× 10	× 7	× 9

3	7	2	8	1	10	7
× 9	× 8	× 7	× 9	× 10	× 11	× 7

3	2	6	5	11	12
× 7	× 10	× 12	× 9	× 7	× 11

Number Correct

___
20

Test 1—Multiplying by 1 to 12

3	4	8	11	10	4	6
× 7	× 6	× 11	× 3	× 2	× 4	× 5

7	9	12	2	7	5	5
× 5	× 10	× 6	× 4	× 8	× 1	× 8

11	8	10	2	12	9
× 6	× 2	× 7	× 5	× 12	× 9

Number Correct

___
20

Test 2—Multiplying by 1 to 12

5	7	4	4	6	2	3
× 2	× 6	× 9	×12	× 6	× 2	× 8

12	11	9	6	10	7	8
× 1	×10	× 8	× 2	×10	× 3	× 5

3	6	3	1	9	8
× 11	× 7	× 4	× 5	× 4	× 7

Number Correct

___
20

Test 3—Multiplying by 1 to 12

11 × 5	4 × 9	9 × 2	7 × 3	4 × 2	10 × 1	2 × 8
10 × 6	8 × 10	5 × 5	8 × 4	8 × 7	7 × 5	10 × 8
4 × 1	9 × 12	11 × 11	6 × 9	6 × 8	9 × 3	

Number Correct

___
20

Test 4—Multiplying by 1 to 12

11 × 7	2 × 5	3 × 2	6 × 5	3 × 6	8 × 5	5 × 4
4 × 4	7 × 10	6 × 8	2 × 7	8 × 1	9 × 6	12 × 3
5 × 12	3 × 7	7 × 11	7 × 9	7 × 2	10 × 8	

Number Correct

___
20

Test 5—Multiplying by 1 to 12

11 × 9	2 × 12	6 × 11	3 × 5	7 × 9	6 × 10	7 × 1
3 × 4	10 × 9	6 × 4	8 × 6	5 × 9	3 × 3	7 × 3
8 × 5	9 × 8	9 × 9	5 × 7	1 × 2	10 × 8	Number Correct ___ 20

Test 6—Multiplying by 1 to 12

2 × 12	8 × 11	3 × 6	9 × 9	10 × 2	3 × 8	10 × 3
5 × 9	7 × 6	3 × 9	5 × 10	9 × 7	12 × 3	11 × 7
1 × 12	10 × 4	7 × 5	6 × 8	5 × 1	4 × 8	Number Correct ___ 20

Test 7—Multiplying by 1 to 12

2 × 7	12 × 2	5 × 6	11 × 8	10 × 5	9 × 6	4 × 1
3 × 11	5 × 12	9 × 3	9 × 8	6 × 7	10 × 4	6 × 3
4 × 10	1 × 9	5 × 9	2 × 9	9 × 7	11 × 9	Number Correct ————— 20

Test 8—Multiplying by 1 to 12

7 × 7	9 × 6	12 × 9	7 × 4	8 × 2	7 × 9	9 × 8
7 × 12	2 × 9	7 × 10	9 × 9	8 × 8	8 × 3	12 × 8
7 × 8	8 × 5	7 × 11	4 × 1	3 × 9	5 × 7	Number Correct ————— 20

Test 9—Multiplying by 1 to 12

7	12	2	11	3	12	9
× 8	× 4	× 10	× 5	× 2	× 3	× 9

10	1	10	4	11	9	2
× 9	× 7	× 12	× 9	× 6	× 8	× 7

9	8	8	2	12	5
× 5	× 11	× 8	× 1	× 9	× 9

Number Correct

___
20

Test 10—Multiplying by 1 to 12

6	11	10	5	2	4	9
× 4	× 1	× 3	× 9	× 5	× 7	× 12

11	4	9	10	6	3	12
× 9	× 11	× 8	× 4	× 9	× 3	× 2

4	5	7	10	1	8
× 8	× 5	× 7	× 6	× 10	× 11

Number Correct

___
20

How Am I Doing?

Tests—Multiplying by 1 to 6

Number correct	Test 1	Test 2	Test 3	Test 4	Test 5	Test 6	Test 7	Test 8	Test 9	Test 10
20										
19										
18										
17										
16										
15										
14										
13										
12										
11										
10										
9										
8										
7										
6										
5										
4										
3										
2										
1										

Tests—Multiplying by 7 to 12

Number correct	Test 1	Test 2	Test 3	Test 4	Test 5	Test 6	Test 7	Test 8	Test 9	Test 10
20										
19										
18										
17										
16										
15										
14										
13										
12										
11										
10										
9										
8										
7										
6										
5										
4										
3										
2										
1										

How Am I Doing?

Tests—Multiplying by 1 to 12

Number correct	Test 1	Test 2	Test 3	Test 4	Test 5	Test 6	Test 7	Test 8	Test 9	Test 10
20										
19										
18										
17										
16										
15										
14										
13										
12										
11										
10										
9										
8										
7										
6										
5										
4										
3										
2										
1										

Test 1—Dividing by 1 to 6

$5\overline{)35}$ $3\overline{)36}$ $5\overline{)25}$ $2\overline{)16}$ $6\overline{)12}$ $6\overline{)24}$ $4\overline{)40}$

$3\overline{)27}$ $1\overline{)3}$ $4\overline{)16}$ $1\overline{)8}$ $6\overline{)18}$ $5\overline{)55}$ $4\overline{)28}$

$4\overline{)44}$ $2\overline{)20}$ $2\overline{)10}$ $6\overline{)72}$ $2\overline{)2}$ $5\overline{)50}$

Number Correct

___
20

Test 2—Dividing by 1 to 6

$2\overline{)20}$ $3\overline{)21}$ $4\overline{)44}$ $2\overline{)18}$ $3\overline{)15}$ $2\overline{)22}$ $3\overline{)12}$

$5\overline{)45}$ $1\overline{)2}$ $3\overline{)6}$ $4\overline{)32}$ $2\overline{)8}$ $5\overline{)60}$ $6\overline{)36}$

$3\overline{)36}$ $5\overline{)35}$ $3\overline{)24}$ $6\overline{)24}$ $6\overline{)66}$ $3\overline{)30}$

Number Correct

___
20

Test 3—Dividing by 1 to 6

$2\overline{)16}$ $4\overline{)48}$ $2\overline{)\ 8}$ $3\overline{)27}$ $5\overline{)25}$ $3\overline{)24}$ $6\overline{)72}$

$6\overline{)30}$ $2\overline{)\ 4}$ $5\overline{)55}$ $6\overline{)36}$ $2\overline{)20}$ $4\overline{)32}$ $5\overline{)45}$

$5\overline{)35}$ $4\overline{)40}$ $5\overline{)15}$ $1\overline{)\ 7}$ $1\overline{)\ 9}$ $2\overline{)12}$

Number Correct

$\overline{20}$

Test 4—Dividing by 1 to 6

$4\overline{)48}$ $1\overline{)11}$ $3\overline{)15}$ $4\overline{)28}$ $5\overline{)20}$ $2\overline{)\ 4}$ $1\overline{)\ 9}$

$4\overline{)36}$ $5\overline{)30}$ $5\overline{)40}$ $2\overline{)\ 6}$ $4\overline{)44}$ $3\overline{)36}$ $6\overline{)60}$

$3\overline{)30}$ $3\overline{)27}$ $5\overline{)25}$ $6\overline{)36}$ $6\overline{)18}$ $2\overline{)16}$

Number Correct

$\overline{20}$

Test 5—Dividing by 1 to 6

$6\overline{)36}$ $2\overline{)6}$ $1\overline{)7}$ $3\overline{)33}$ $3\overline{)3}$ $5\overline{)10}$ $5\overline{)25}$

$4\overline{)24}$ $3\overline{)15}$ $2\overline{)14}$ $2\overline{)8}$ $6\overline{)30}$ $4\overline{)44}$ $3\overline{)12}$

$6\overline{)72}$ $2\overline{)20}$ $4\overline{)32}$ $3\overline{)27}$ $1\overline{)12}$ $5\overline{)45}$

Number Correct

___
20

Test 6—Dividing by 1 to 6

$5\overline{)60}$ $5\overline{)15}$ $1\overline{)2}$ $4\overline{)36}$ $6\overline{)12}$ $5\overline{)50}$ $6\overline{)18}$

$2\overline{)12}$ $1\overline{)11}$ $3\overline{)33}$ $3\overline{)36}$ $2\overline{)14}$ $4\overline{)40}$ $5\overline{)35}$

$2\overline{)10}$ $4\overline{)32}$ $1\overline{)9}$ $6\overline{)24}$ $2\overline{)18}$ $2\overline{)4}$

Number Correct

___
20

Test 7—Dividing by 1 to 6

$2\overline{)20}$ $2\overline{)14}$ $5\overline{)30}$ $3\overline{)21}$ $4\overline{)36}$ $2\overline{)10}$ $6\overline{)66}$

$6\overline{)36}$ $2\overline{)24}$ $6\overline{)30}$ $3\overline{)12}$ $4\overline{)48}$ $5\overline{)50}$ $5\overline{)45}$

$3\overline{)9}$ $3\overline{)15}$ $5\overline{)20}$ $4\overline{)44}$ $3\overline{)24}$ $1\overline{)10}$

Number Correct

$\overline{20}$

Test 8—Dividing by 1 to 6

$4\overline{)32}$ $3\overline{)9}$ $3\overline{)18}$ $6\overline{)48}$ $5\overline{)60}$ $5\overline{)50}$ $1\overline{)1}$

$2\overline{)6}$ $4\overline{)16}$ $6\overline{)60}$ $3\overline{)27}$ $3\overline{)15}$ $4\overline{)44}$ $2\overline{)20}$

$5\overline{)45}$ $4\overline{)12}$ $2\overline{)12}$ $6\overline{)72}$ $3\overline{)21}$ $5\overline{)30}$

Number Correct

$\overline{20}$

Test 9—Dividing by 1 to 6

$2 \overline{)22}$ $1 \overline{)9}$ $6 \overline{)72}$ $4 \overline{)32}$ $6 \overline{)66}$ $5 \overline{)10}$ $3 \overline{)18}$

$1 \overline{)3}$ $5 \overline{)35}$ $2 \overline{)20}$ $6 \overline{)24}$ $3 \overline{)21}$ $4 \overline{)44}$ $5 \overline{)15}$

$4 \overline{)40}$ $2 \overline{)24}$ $3 \overline{)9}$ $2 \overline{)16}$ $2 \overline{)12}$ $5 \overline{)25}$

Number Correct

$\overline{}$
20

Test 10—Dividing by 1 to 6

$2 \overline{)14}$ $4 \overline{)32}$ $3 \overline{)6}$ $4 \overline{)16}$ $6 \overline{)30}$ $5 \overline{)50}$ $3 \overline{)27}$

$2 \overline{)20}$ $6 \overline{)18}$ $1 \overline{)2}$ $5 \overline{)55}$ $3 \overline{)9}$ $4 \overline{)48}$ $6 \overline{)12}$

$4 \overline{)4}$ $5 \overline{)35}$ $3 \overline{)24}$ $1 \overline{)9}$ $2 \overline{)4}$ $3 \overline{)18}$

Number Correct

$\overline{}$
20

Test 1—Dividing by 7 to 12

$10\overline{)10}$ ¹ $12\overline{)24}$ ² $9\overline{)81}$ ⁹ $8\overline{)88}$ ¹¹ $11\overline{)66}$ ⁶ $8\overline{)64}$ ⁸ $7\overline{)84}$ ¹²

$7\overline{)42}$ ⁶ $7\overline{)77}$ ¹¹ $9\overline{)36}$ ⁴ $11\overline{)55}$ ⁵ $8\overline{)72}$ ⁹ $10\overline{)60}$ ⁶ $12\overline{)48}$ ⁴

$7\overline{)49}$ ⁷ $10\overline{)100}$ ¹⁰ $8\overline{)48}$ ⁶ $12\overline{)36}$ ³ $8\overline{)56}$ ⁷ $10\overline{)120}$ ¹²

Number Correct

_____
20

Test 2—Dividing by 7 to 12

$9\overline{)99}$ $7\overline{)63}$ $12\overline{)24}$ $10\overline{)110}$ $7\overline{)35}$ $9\overline{)36}$ $8\overline{)24}$

$12\overline{)84}$ $7\overline{)42}$ $9\overline{)18}$ $8\overline{)80}$ $9\overline{)72}$ $9\overline{)90}$ $10\overline{)120}$

$8\overline{)48}$ $10\overline{)70}$ $11\overline{)44}$ $11\overline{)66}$ $11\overline{)55}$ $7\overline{)21}$

Number Correct

_____
20

Test 3—Dividing by 7 to 12

$7 \overline{)70}$ $10 \overline{)10}$ $12 \overline{)144}$ $8 \overline{)32}$ $11 \overline{)66}$ $10 \overline{)30}$ $10 \overline{)50}$

$7 \overline{)84}$ $9 \overline{)108}$ $7 \overline{)42}$ $9 \overline{)72}$ $10 \overline{)30}$ $7 \overline{)28}$ $12 \overline{)60}$

$8 \overline{)48}$ $9 \overline{)54}$ $11 \overline{)121}$ $8 \overline{)56}$ $8 \overline{)72}$ $9 \overline{)45}$

Number
Correct

_____

20

Test 4—Dividing by 7 to 12

$9 \overline{)99}$ $7 \overline{)49}$ $12 \overline{)24}$ $8 \overline{)40}$ $10 \overline{)30}$ $11 \overline{)88}$ $12 \overline{)48}$

$7 \overline{)70}$ $9 \overline{)36}$ $7 \overline{)42}$ $10 \overline{)120}$ $9 \overline{)108}$ $12 \overline{)12}$ $10 \overline{)100}$

$8 \overline{)88}$ $11 \overline{)66}$ $7 \overline{)14}$ $8 \overline{)24}$ $10 \overline{)60}$ $8 \overline{)72}$

Number
Correct

_____

20

Test 5—Dividing by 7 to 12

9)54   7)21   8)16   8)80   10)90   8)48   10)70

12)48   11)55   8)56   7)77   11)121   7)56   9)9

10)100   9)18   12)60   9)81   11)99   12)144

Number Correct

___
20

Test 6—Dividing by 7 to 12

7)84   12)36   12)48   9)81   8)32   12)60   11)66

10)30   9)72   7)28   7)14   8)40   7)56   7)35

11)121   8)88   10)80   10)100   10)120   9)45

Number Correct

___
20

Test 7—Dividing by 7 to 12

$12)\overline{36}$ $7)\overline{35}$ $9)\overline{36}$ $12)\overline{48}$ $7)\overline{56}$ $12)\overline{120}$ $7)\overline{42}$

$8)\overline{48}$ $9)\overline{63}$ $12)\overline{60}$ $10)\overline{50}$ $11)\overline{44}$ $10)\overline{120}$ $8)\overline{88}$

$7)\overline{84}$ $10)\overline{90}$ $9)\overline{81}$ $8)\overline{80}$ $9)\overline{54}$ $10)\overline{30}$

Number Correct

___
20

Test 8—Dividing by 7 to 12

$10)\overline{50}$ $7)\overline{42}$ $9)\overline{27}$ $12)\overline{132}$ $9)\overline{18}$ $8)\overline{64}$ $9)\overline{72}$

$8)\overline{16}$ $10)\overline{120}$ $7)\overline{63}$ $11)\overline{77}$ $7)\overline{28}$ $12)\overline{36}$ $9)\overline{36}$

$10)\overline{100}$ $12)\overline{48}$ $10)\overline{60}$ $8)\overline{24}$ $9)\overline{54}$ $9)\overline{90}$

Number Correct

___
20

Test 9—Dividing by 7 to 12

$11\overline{)88}$ $7\overline{)42}$ $8\overline{)48}$ $9\overline{)27}$ $7\overline{)49}$ $11\overline{)66}$ $12\overline{)60}$

$8\overline{)16}$ $10\overline{)50}$ $9\overline{)99}$ $10\overline{)60}$ $7\overline{)7}$ $8\overline{)24}$ $7\overline{)70}$

$11\overline{)77}$ $7\overline{)21}$ $9\overline{)72}$ $12\overline{)144}$ $8\overline{)64}$ $10\overline{)40}$

Number Correct

___
20

Test 10—Dividing by 7 to 12

$9\overline{)36}$ $7\overline{)56}$ $8\overline{)40}$ $12\overline{)12}$ $9\overline{)18}$ $8\overline{)80}$ $10\overline{)60}$

$9\overline{)54}$ $10\overline{)40}$ $12\overline{)36}$ $7\overline{)70}$ $11\overline{)99}$ $10\overline{)70}$ $9\overline{)27}$

$10\overline{)20}$ $7\overline{)84}$ $8\overline{)64}$ $12\overline{)84}$ $7\overline{)77}$ $12\overline{)48}$

Number Correct

___
20

Test 1—Dividing by 1 to 12

$5\overline{)25}$ $8\overline{)32}$ $5\overline{)15}$ $3\overline{)30}$ $11\overline{)99}$ $6\overline{)72}$ $3\overline{)27}$

$2\overline{)2}$ $2\overline{)16}$ $12\overline{)120}$ $6\overline{)60}$ $8\overline{)56}$ $9\overline{)63}$ $4\overline{)16}$

$7\overline{)63}$ $7\overline{)35}$ $3\overline{)33}$ $1\overline{)12}$ $4\overline{)40}$ $10\overline{)50}$

Number Correct

___

20

Test 2—Dividing by 1 to 12

$5\overline{)30}$ $2\overline{)10}$ $9\overline{)9}$ $1\overline{)10}$ $7\overline{)84}$ $9\overline{)27}$ $11\overline{)66}$

$12\overline{)108}$ $10\overline{)80}$ $4\overline{)32}$ $5\overline{)60}$ $9\overline{)99}$ $4\overline{)8}$ $4\overline{)36}$

$6\overline{)42}$ $7\overline{)63}$ $8\overline{)32}$ $9\overline{)45}$ $3\overline{)6}$ $1\overline{)35}$

Number Correct

___

20

Test 3—Dividing by 1 to 12

$5\overline{)45}$ $1\overline{)11}$ $3\overline{)27}$ $4\overline{)12}$ $7\overline{)56}$ $7\overline{)7}$ $10\overline{)120}$

$2\overline{)20}$ $1\overline{)6}$ $2\overline{)24}$ $9\overline{)72}$ $8\overline{)40}$ $8\overline{)80}$ $12\overline{)36}$

$10\overline{)100}$ $6\overline{)6}$ $5\overline{)30}$ $6\overline{)42}$ $9\overline{)108}$ $11\overline{)66}$

Number Correct

___
20

Test 4—Dividing by 1 to 12

$6\overline{)24}$ $10\overline{)70}$ $7\overline{)42}$ $11\overline{)132}$ $5\overline{)50}$ $9\overline{)81}$ $12\overline{)12}$

$2\overline{)24}$ $12\overline{)36}$ $12\overline{)96}$ $3\overline{)18}$ $4\overline{)40}$ $8\overline{)64}$ $5\overline{)55}$

$9\overline{)36}$ $7\overline{)77}$ $5\overline{)60}$ $2\overline{)14}$ $10\overline{)40}$ $11\overline{)55}$

Number Correct

___
20

Test 5—Dividing by 1 to 12

$3\overline{)24}$ $6\overline{)30}$ $8\overline{)88}$ $4\overline{)28}$ $7\overline{)84}$ $10\overline{)50}$ $5\overline{)55}$

$12\overline{)84}$ $11\overline{)110}$ $7\overline{)56}$ $8\overline{)8}$ $4\overline{)40}$ $3\overline{)15}$ $2\overline{)22}$

$12\overline{)24}$ $11\overline{)88}$ $9\overline{)90}$ $1\overline{)7}$ $8\overline{)72}$ $6\overline{)36}$

Number Correct

$\overline{}$
20

Test 6—Dividing by 1 to 12

$5\overline{)40}$ $10\overline{)100}$ $11\overline{)77}$ $7\overline{)14}$ $8\overline{)64}$ $6\overline{)42}$ $1\overline{)6}$

$6\overline{)54}$ $4\overline{)16}$ $2\overline{)24}$ $10\overline{)70}$ $8\overline{)80}$ $3\overline{)36}$ $7\overline{)28}$

$11\overline{)121}$ $7\overline{)35}$ $5\overline{)25}$ $12\overline{)48}$ $9\overline{)99}$ $8\overline{)48}$

Number Correct

$\overline{}$
20

Test 7—Dividing by 1 to 12

$7\overline{)35}$ $9\overline{)108}$ $4\overline{)32}$ $9\overline{)81}$ $2\overline{)22}$ $8\overline{)72}$ $6\overline{)36}$

$10\overline{)60}$ $2\overline{)20}$ $1\overline{)8}$ $8\overline{)16}$ $4\overline{)40}$ $9\overline{)45}$ $3\overline{)21}$

$12\overline{)144}$ $6\overline{)12}$ $11\overline{)33}$ $8\overline{)40}$ $4\overline{)44}$ $5\overline{)20}$

Number Correct

____
20

Test 8—Dividing by 1 to 12

$11\overline{)132}$ $10\overline{)20}$ $8\overline{)40}$ $12\overline{)120}$ $10\overline{)50}$ $9\overline{)99}$ $8\overline{)32}$

$6\overline{)72}$ $4\overline{)24}$ $5\overline{)35}$ $9\overline{)108}$ $7\overline{)7}$ $4\overline{)40}$ $3\overline{)24}$

$5\overline{)55}$ $9\overline{)63}$ $6\overline{)48}$ $1\overline{)4}$ $2\overline{)10}$ $8\overline{)24}$

Number Correct

____
20

Test 9—Dividing by 1 to 12

$12\overline{)144}$ $\quad$ $6\overline{)48}$ $\quad$ $6\overline{)66}$ $\quad$ $4\overline{)8}$ $\quad$ $7\overline{)28}$ $\quad$ $10\overline{)90}$ $\quad$ $1\overline{)3}$

$9\overline{)27}$ $\quad$ $7\overline{)49}$ $\quad$ $10\overline{)30}$ $\quad$ $7\overline{)77}$ $\quad$ $9\overline{)54}$ $\quad$ $8\overline{)80}$ $\quad$ $9\overline{)18}$

$5\overline{)30}$ $\quad$ $11\overline{)132}$ $\quad$ $2\overline{)2}$ $\quad$ $3\overline{)27}$ $\quad$ $11\overline{)55}$ $\quad$ $8\overline{)48}$

Number Correct

___
20

Test 10—Dividing by 1 to 12

$3\overline{)27}$ $\quad$ $4\overline{)16}$ $\quad$ $7\overline{)70}$ $\quad$ $8\overline{)80}$ $\quad$ $11\overline{)121}$ $\quad$ $6\overline{)48}$ $\quad$ $12\overline{)72}$

$5\overline{)25}$ $\quad$ $9\overline{)36}$ $\quad$ $12\overline{)36}$ $\quad$ $5\overline{)50}$ $\quad$ $10\overline{)70}$ $\quad$ $4\overline{)20}$ $\quad$ $8\overline{)24}$

$2\overline{)18}$ $\quad$ $12\overline{)96}$ $\quad$ $7\overline{)63}$ $\quad$ $1\overline{)2}$ $\quad$ $3\overline{)36}$ $\quad$ $9\overline{)81}$

Number Correct

___
20

How Am I Doing?

Tests—Dividing by 1 to 6

Number correct	Test 1	Test 2	Test 3	Test 4	Test 5	Test 6	Test 7	Test 8	Test 9	Test 10
20										
19										
18										
17										
16										
15										
14										
13										
12										
11										
10										
9										
8										
7										
6										
5										
4										
3										
2										
1										

Tests—Dividing by 7 to 12

Number correct	Test 1	Test 2	Test 3	Test 4	Test 5	Test 6	Test 7	Test 8	Test 9	Test 10
20										
19										
18										
17										
16										
15										
14										
13										
12										
11										
10										
9										
8										
7										
6										
5										
4										
3										
2										
1										

How Am I Doing?

Tests—Dividing by 1 to 12

Number correct	Test 1	Test 2	Test 3	Test 4	Test 5	Test 6	Test 7	Test 8	Test 9	Test 10
20										
19										
18										
17										
16										
15										
14										
13										
12										
11										
10										
9										
8										
7										
6										
5										
4										
3										
2										
1										

Metric Units and Measurement

				Base Unit			
Length	Kilometre km	Hectometre (hm)	Decametre (dam)	Metre (m)	Decimetre (dm)	Centimetre (cm)	Millimetre (mm)
Weight	Kilogram (kg)	Hectogram (hg)	Decagram (dag)	Gram (g)	Decigram (dg)	Centigram (cg)	Milligram (mg)
Volume	Kilolitre (kL)	Hectolitre (hL)	Decalitre (daL)	Litre (L)	Decilitre (dL)	Centilitre (cL)	Millilitre (mL)
How many are in 1 metre/ gram/litre?	.001	.01	.1	1	10	100	1000
How many metres/ grams/litres are in this?	1000	100	10	1	.1	.01	.001
	⟵ **Bigger**			**Base Unit**	**Smaller** ⟶		

Math Glossary

A

Above: In or at a place that is higher.

Acute: An angle that measures less than 90°.

Acute Triangle: A triangle with three acute angles.

Addend: Any number used to add to get a sum. In 7 + 2 = 9, the addends are 7 and 2.

Addition: An operation where two or more numbers are combined.

Algebra: An area of math where numbers are represented by letters.

Algebraic Expression: A mathematical phrase that can have numbers, letters, and operation signs. It does not have an equal sign.

Algorithm: A set of steps to follow for carrying out a calculation.

Always: At all times.

Amount: A quantity, number of, total, sum, or size.

Analogue Clock: A tool used to show the time. It has moving hands and hours marked from 1 to 12.

Angle: The figure formed when two lines meet at a vertex.

Approximately: To come close to or be nearly the same as.

Area: The space a surface takes up. Area is measured in square units.

Array: Numbers or objects arranged in rows and columns.

Attribute: A characteristic that describes something. Colour and size are examples.

Axis: A real or imaginary reference line. X-axis: the horizontal axis of a graph. Y-axis: the vertical axis of a graph.

B

Bar Graph: A graph that uses horizontal or vertical bars to show data.

Base Ten: A number system based on ten.

Behind: At the back or rear.

Below: In or at a place that is lower than another object.

Benchmark: A standard by which something can be measured. A reference to help judge.

Beside: At the side of or next to.

Between: In a space that separates objects or times.

Broken Line Graph: A graph that uses points to show data. The points are sometimes connected with a line.

C

Calculate: To figure out by computation.

Cardinal Direction: The main points of a compass—north, east, south, and west.

Cartesian Plane: A plane containing two perpendicular axes (*x* and *y*).

Capacity: The amount a container can hold.

Celsius: A temperature measurement scale used in the metric system. For example, 0° is the temperature of freezing water.

Centimetre: A metric unit used for measuring length. 100 cm = 1m

Century: A period of time equal to 100 years.

Certain: An event that will definitely happen.

Chance: The likelihood that a particular outcome will happen.

Circle Graph: A graph that uses a circle divided into sectors to represent data. Also called a pie chart.

Circumference: The distance around a circle. Circumference = 2 × 3.14 × radius, or C = 2πr.

Classify: To arrange and order.

Clock: A tool that measures and shows time.

Collect: To bring together.

Compare: To find what is the same and what is different about numbers or objects.

Conclusion: The result or outcome of an act or process.

Constant: A number that does not change.

Coordinates: The values in an ordered pair that can be shown on a coordinate grid.

Coordinate Systems: An ordered pair of numbers that show location.

Concrete Graph: A graph where real objects are used to represent data.

Congruent: Having the same shape and size.

Coin: A piece of metal used as money.

D

Data: A collection of information that is often shown on tables or graphs.

Decade: A period of time equal to 10 years.

Decimal Point: The point which separates the integer and fraction parts of a number.

Decimal System: A number system that is based on 10. Also called the base 10 system.

Decomposition: A way to separate a number into parts.

Decrease: To get smaller.

* Define: State the meaning of something.

Degree: A unit for measuring the size of angles. For example, 60°

Denominator: The number of parts that a whole is divided into. It is the bottom number of a fraction.

* Describe: Express an idea using words, numbers, and pictures.

* Determine: To find out exactly.

Diagram: A drawing that represents something.

Diameter: A straight line passing through the centre of a circle touching two points on the edge of the circumference.

Difference: The result of subtraction.

Digit: A symbol used to make a number. 0, 1, 2, 3, 4, 5, 6, 7, 8, and 9 are the digits we use to make numbers such as 12.

Dime: A Canadian or American coin valued at 10 cents.

Discrete Data: Data that has a certain number of possible values.

Distance: The length between points.

Division: An operation where a quantity is grouped into equal parts. See <u>multiplication</u> for definition.

Double: Twice as much.

E

Edge: Where two faces of a 3-D object meet.

Elapsed Time: The measured duration of an event.

Equal: Having the same value.

Equality: The state of being equal.

Equation: A mathematical sentence that uses an equal sign that shows two expressions are equal.

Equilateral: Having all sides or faces equal.

Equivalent Fractions: Fractions that have the same value but may have different numerators and denominators.

Estimate: To approximate an answer. Rounding is an example.

Even Number: A number that can be divided evenly by two.

Event: Possible outcome(s) in an experiment.

Expanded Form: A way of writing numbers that shows the value of each digit. An example is 200 + 40 + 1.

Experiment: A test to discover something unknown, or to verify something expected.

* Explain: To offer reasons and/or to justify.

Expression: One or a group of mathematical symbols representing a number or quantity.

F

Face: One surface of a 3-D object.

Factors: Numbers that are multiplied to produce a product.

Fair: When events are equally likely.

Favourable Outcome: Positive results.

Few: A small number.

Flip: To turn over.

Fraction: A number that represents part of a group or a whole.

Frequency: The number of times an event occurs.

G

Graph: A drawing or diagram used to record information.

Greater Than: More than.

Grouping: Dividing things into equal groups or sets.

Growing Pattern: A pattern where the terms become larger.

H

Height: A measurement from top to bottom.

Horizontal: Parallel to the horizon.

Hour: A unit of time that is equal to 60 minutes.

I

* Investigate: To explore or research by problem solving.

Impossible: An event that cannot happen.

Improper Fraction: A fraction whose numerator is larger than the denominator.

Increase: To get larger.

Inequality: Not equal in size, amount, or value.

Interpret: To translate or analyse.

Intersecting Lines: Two lines that cross.

Interval: The distance between two points.

Inverse Operations: Two operations that are opposite. Addition is the opposite of subtraction. 2 + 3 = 5 5 to 2 = 3

Isosceles: A triangle with two equal sides and two angles the same size.

J

* Justify: To support or defend.

K

Kilogram: A metric unit for measuring mass (weight). 1 kilogram (kg) = 1000 grams (g)

Kilometre: A metric unit for measuring distance (km). 1 kilometre (km) = 1000 metres (m)

L

Least: The smallest number in a group or a set of data.

Length: The measurement of distance between two points.

Less: Not as many as another number.

Likelihood: A chance that an outcome will happen.

Likely: An event that is expected to happen more than half the time.

Line: A length (straight or curved) without breadth or thickness.

* List: To itemize or tally.

Litre: A metric unit of capacity.

Location: The place or position of an object.

M

Many: A large number, the opposite of few.

Mass: The quantity of matter in an object, often measured in grams or kilograms.

Mean: The sum of a set of values divided by the number of values in the set. It is also referred to as the average.

Measure: Using standard units to find a size or a quantity.

Median: The middle value in an ordered set of values. The values are lined up in order from the smallest to the largest to find the middle value.

Metre: A metric unit used for measuring length.

Metric System: A decimal system of measurement using multiples of ten.

Millennium: A period of time equal to 1000 years.

Millimetre: A metric unit for measuring length. 10 mm = 1 cm

Mixed Number: A number written as a whole number and a fraction.

Mode: The most frequently occurring value in a set of values.

More likely: An event that will probably occur.

More: The greater amount.

Most: The greatest amount.

Multiplication: An operation where a number is added to itself a number of times.

N

Net: A flat shape that can be folded into a 3-D object.

Never: Absolutely not. The probability is zero.

Nickel: A Canadian or American coin valued at 5 cents.

Non standard: Objects, such as paper clips, used as measurement units.

Numerator: The number above the line in a fraction.

* **Words** = problem solving words

O

Obtuse Angle: Any angle between 90° and 180°.

Obtuse Triangle: A triangle with one obtuse angle.

Odd Number: A number that can not be divided evenly by two.

Operation: In arithmetic there are four operations to solve problems: addition, subtraction, multiplication, and division.

Ordered Pair: A pair of numbers used to locate a point on a coordinate grid. An example is (9, 12).

Ordinal Number: A number that shows a place or position.

Outcome: The different ways that an event can happen in a probability experiment.

P

Parallel: Lines that are the same distance apart and never cross.

Parallelogram: A quadrilateral where the opposite sides are parallel and equal in length.

Pattern: An arrangements of shapes, numbers, or objects that repeat.

Penny: An American coin valued at 1 cent.

Pentagon: A polygon with five sides.

Perimeter: The distance around a shape or an object.

Pictograph: A graph that shows data using pictures.

Place Value: The value of a digit depending on its position in a number.

Polyhedron: Three-dimensional figures with plane faces.

Polygon: A closed shape having three or more sides.

* **Predict:** Describe what may happen based on the information provided in the question.

Primary Data: Data observed or collected directly from first-hand knowledge.

Prime Number: A whole number that has only two factors. It can be divided evenly only by one and itself. (2, 3, 5, 7, and 11 are some examples)

Prism: A 3-D object with two bases that are parallel and congruent.

Probability: The chance or likelihood of something happening.

Probably: An event that might occur.

Product: The answer when two numbers are multiplied. The product of 2 and 4 is 8.

Pyramid: A 3-D object with a polygon as a base and triangular faces that taper to the same vertex.

Q

Quadrant: Any quarter of a plane divided by an *x* and *y* axis.

Quadrilateral: A polygon having four sides.

Quantity: Amount of something.

Quarter: A Canadian or American coin valued at 25 cents.

Quotient: The answer after dividing one number by another one. For example, the quotient of 6 ÷ 2 is 3.

R

Range: The difference of the highest number and lowest number in a set of data.

Ray: A line that has a starting point but no endpoint.

Ratio: A comparative value of two or more amounts. An example is 2:4 or as a fraction.

Reasoning: Evidence or arguments used in thinking or forming conclusions.

Reciprocal: One of two numbers whose products are 1.

Rectangle: A quadrilateral with four right angles and two pairs of opposite equal parallel sides. Length and width can be either equal or unequal.

Rectangular Prism: A prism with rectangular faces.

Reflection: A mirror image of a shape or an object.

Remainder: The amount left over after dividing a number.

Represent: To show.

Rhombus: A type of quadrilateral, a parallelogram with four equal sides and opposite angles.

Right Angle: An angle which is equal to 90°.

Right Angled Triangle: A triangle with one angle measuring 90°.

Rotation: A circular movement where a central point is fixed and everything else moves around that point.

Rotational Symmetry: When a shape or image is rotated and still looks the same. This image can be rotated to three different positions and it would always look the same.

Round: To change a number to a more convienient number. For example, to round 22 to the nearest 10 is 20.

S

Scalene: A triangle where no sides are equal.

Secondary Data: Data collected by someone other than the user.

Set: A collection of items.

Sequence: An ordered set of numbers, shapes, or other mathematical objects that are arranged accoding to a rule.

* Show Your Work: Use pictures, words, numbers, diagrams, symbols, and graphs to show your thinking as you arrived at your solution.

Side: One of the lines that make up a 2-D shape.

Simplify: To reduce the numerator and denominator in a fraction or to the smallest numbers possible.

Skeleton: An outline or sketch.

Skip Count: Counting forward or backward using a specific multiple or interval.

Slide: To move an item in the same direction without rotating it.

Sort: To organize according to shape, colour, or number.

Square-Based Pyramid: A pyramid with a square base.

Square: A quadrilateral with four equal sides, four right angles, and four lines of symmetry. The opposite sides are parallel.

Standard: Using a measurement unit as a means for measure.

Stem and Leaf Plot: A data display where groups of data are arranged by place value.

* Strategy: A plan, or way to solve a problem or get to an answer.

Subtraction: An operation where one number is taken away from another number.

Sum: The result of addition.

Surface area: Total area of a surface of a 3-D, and is measured in square units.

Survey: A method of collecting data.

Symmetry: An object has symmetry if one half of the object is a mirror image of the other half.

T

Table: An organizer that shows data in rows and columns.

Tally: Using marks to record counts or votes.

Tangram: An ancient Chinese puzzle based on a square cut into seven pieces.

Temperature: A measurement of how hot or cold something is.

Tenth: One part of ten equal parts.

Term: One of the numbers in a sequence or series of numbers.

Three-Dimensional Object: A figure that has height, depth, and width. Written as 3-D.

Time: Time is the ongoing sequence of events taking place. Time is measured using clocks and other timing devices.

Transformation: A change in position or size.

Translation: Also called a slide, moves every point on a shape in the same direction and over the same distance.

Triangular Prism: A polyhedron, a prism with two identical triangular bases.

Turn: To rotate.

Two-Dimensional Shapes: A shape that has only width and height and no thickness. Written as 2-D.

U

Unit: Another name for one.

Unlikely: An event that is expected to happen less than half the time.

V

Value: A numerical amount.

Variable: A quantity that can change. It is a symbol for a number that has not yet been determined. An example is x.

Venn diagram: A diagram using circles or other shapes showing relationships among sets of data.

Vertex: An example is *x* in 2-D geometry, where two lines meet. In 3-D geometry, where three or more edges meet. The plural of vertex is vertices.

Vertical: In an up-down position.

Volume: The amount of space an object occupies. Volume is measured in cubic units.

W

Weight: The measure of how heavy something is.

Whole Number: Any number used for counting, including zero.

Width: The distance across from one side to the other.

X

x-axis: The horizontal axis of a graph.

x-cooridinate: The position of a point along the x-axis. The *x* coordinate is written first in an ordered pair of coordinates (*x,y*).

Y

y-axis: The vertical axis of a graph.

y-coordinate: The position of a point along the y axis. The *y* coordinate is written second in an ordered pair of coordinates (*x,y*).

Aa

Trace and write. Circle your best *A* or *a* on each line.

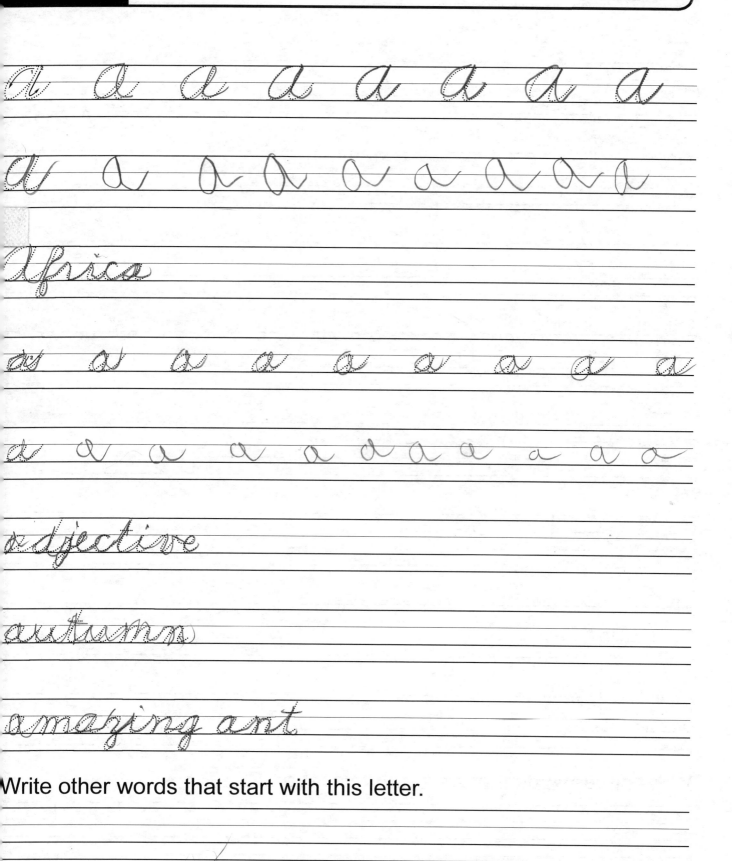

Write other words that start with this letter.

Trace and write. Circle your best $\mathcal{B}$ or b on each line.

$\mathcal{B}$ $\mathcal{B}$ $\mathcal{B}$ $\mathcal{B}$ $\mathcal{B}$ $\mathcal{B}$ $\mathcal{B}$ $\mathcal{B}$ $\mathcal{B}$

$\mathcal{B}$

Banff

b b b b b b b b b

b

baseball

bluebird

brilliant bird

Write other words that start with this letter.

Cc

Trace and write. Circle your best *C* or *c* on each line.

C C C C C C C C C C

C

Canadian

c c c c c c c c c c c

c

crayon

clarinet

curious cat

Write other words that start with this letter.

Trace and write. Circle your best _D_ or _d_ on each line.

𝒟 𝒟 𝒟 𝒟 𝒟 𝒟 𝒟 𝒟 𝒟

𝒟

Douglas

d d d d d d d d d

d

drone

devoted

delayed dinner

Write other words that start with this letter.

Ee

Trace and write. Circle your best *E* or *e* on each line.

E E E E E E E E E

E

Egypt

e e e e e e e e e

e

equal

emerald

eat elderberries

Write other words that start with this letter.

Ff

Trace and write. Circle your best *F* or *f* on each line.

F F F F F F F F F

F

France

f f f f f f f f f

f

fireworks

flipper

funny fish

Write other words that start with this letter.

Trace and write. Circle your best 𝒢 or 𝑔 on each line.

𝒢 𝒢 𝒢 𝒢 𝒢 𝒢 𝒢 𝒢 𝒢 𝒢

𝒢

Greece

𝑔 𝑔 𝑔 𝑔 𝑔 𝑔 𝑔 𝑔 𝑔 𝑔

𝑔

goldfish

glacier

gigantic grape

Write other words that start with this letter.

Trace and write. Circle your best *H* or *h* on each line.

H H H H H H H H H H

H

Hamilton

h h h h h h h h h h

h

hydrant

habitat

hopping hare

Write other words that start with this letter.

Trace and write. Circle your best ℓ or i on each line.

ℓ ℓ ℓ ℓ ℓ ℓ ℓ ℓ ℓ ℓ

ℓ

ℓqaluit

i i i i i i i i i i

i

island

imitation

interesting idea

Write other words that start with this letter.

Trace and write. Circle your best *J* or *j* on each line.

J J J J J J J J J J J

J

Jennifer

j j j j j j j j j j j

j

jamboree

janitor

juicy jujube

Write other words that start with this letter.

Kk

Trace and write. Circle your best K or k on each line.

K K K K K K K K K

K

Kenya

k k k k k k k k k

k

koala

kumquat

kooky kitten

Write other words that start with this letter.

Trace and write. Circle your best $\mathscr{L}$ or $\mathscr{l}$ on each line.

$\mathscr{L}$ $\mathscr{L}$ $\mathscr{L}$ $\mathscr{L}$ $\mathscr{L}$ $\mathscr{L}$ $\mathscr{L}$ $\mathscr{L}$ $\mathscr{L}$

$\mathscr{L}$

London

$\mathscr{l}$ $\mathscr{l}$ $\mathscr{l}$ $\mathscr{l}$ $\mathscr{l}$ $\mathscr{l}$ $\mathscr{l}$ $\mathscr{l}$ $\mathscr{l}$

$\mathscr{l}$

laundry

lobster

lemon lime

Write other words that start with this letter.

Trace and write. Circle your best *M* or *m* on each line.

m *m* *m* *m* *m* *m* *m* *m*

m

madagascar

m *m* *m* *m* *m* *m* *m* *m*

m

mailbox

millipede

moist melon

Write other words that start with this letter.

Trace and write. Circle your best n or m on each line.

n n n n n n n n n

n

nunavut

m m m m m m m m m

m

nutmeg

nothing

mice meat

Write other words that start with this letter.

Oo

Trace and write. Circle your best O or o on each line.

O O O O O O O O O O

O

Ottawa

o o o o o o o o o o

o

omnivore

oyster

odd octopus

Write other words that start with this letter.

Pp

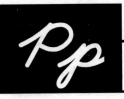

Trace and write. Circle your best P or p on each line.

P P P P P P P P P

P

Peru

p p p p p p p p

p

propeller

platypus

perfect peach

Write other words that start with this letter.

Trace and write. Circle your best *Q* or *q* on each line.

Q Q Q Q Q Q Q Q Q Q Q

Q

Québec

q q q q q q q q q

q

quartz

qualify

quiz question

Write other words that start with this letter.

Trace and write. Circle your best R or r on each line.

R R R R R R R R

R

Russia

r r r r r r r r

r

raccoon

rhubarb

rare rainbow

Write other words that start with this letter.

Trace and write. Circle your best _S_ or _s_ on each line.

_S S S S S S S S S S_

_S_

Saturn

_s s s s s s s s s s_

_s_

skeleton

scorpion

slippery slope

Write other words that start with this letter.

Trace and write. Circle your best $\mathcal{T}$ or t on each line.

$\mathcal{T}$ $\mathcal{T}$ $\mathcal{T}$ $\mathcal{T}$ $\mathcal{T}$ $\mathcal{T}$ $\mathcal{T}$ $\mathcal{T}$ $\mathcal{T}$ $\mathcal{T}$

$\mathcal{T}$

Timbuktu

t t t t t t t t t

t

thousand

tangerine

tiny tuatara

Write other words that start with this letter.

Uu

Trace and write. Circle your best *U* or *u* on each line.

U U U U U U U U U U

U

Uranus

u u u u u u u u u

u

umbrella

utensils

used unicycle

Write other words that start with this letter.

Trace and write. Circle your best $\mathcal{V}$ or $\mathcal{v}$ on each line.

$\mathcal{V}$ $\mathcal{V}$ $\mathcal{V}$ $\mathcal{V}$ $\mathcal{V}$ $\mathcal{V}$ $\mathcal{V}$ $\mathcal{V}$ $\mathcal{V}$ $\mathcal{V}$

$\mathcal{V}$

Venus

$\mathcal{v}$ $\mathcal{v}$ $\mathcal{v}$ $\mathcal{v}$ $\mathcal{v}$ $\mathcal{v}$ $\mathcal{v}$ $\mathcal{v}$ $\mathcal{v}$ $\mathcal{v}$

$\mathcal{v}$

valley

volcano

vibrant velvet

Write other words that start with this letter.

Trace and write. Circle your best *W* or *w* on each line.

W W W W W W W W W

W

Waterloo

w w w w w w w w w

w

wild

walnut

wet wallpaper

Write other words that start with this letter.

Trace and write. Circle your best $\mathcal{X}$ or x on each line.

$\mathcal{X}$ $\mathcal{X}$ $\mathcal{X}$ $\mathcal{X}$ $\mathcal{X}$ $\mathcal{X}$ $\mathcal{X}$ $\mathcal{X}$ $\mathcal{X}$ $\mathcal{X}$

$\mathcal{X}$

Xavier

x x x x x x x x x x

x

axe

exit

xylophone

Write other words that start with this letter.

Trace and write. Circle your best $\mathcal{Y}$ or y on each line.

$\mathcal{Y}$ $\mathcal{Y}$ $\mathcal{Y}$ $\mathcal{Y}$ $\mathcal{Y}$ $\mathcal{Y}$ $\mathcal{Y}$ $\mathcal{Y}$ $\mathcal{Y}$ $\mathcal{Y}$ $\mathcal{Y}$

$\mathcal{Y}$

Yellowknife

y y y y y y y y

y

youngster

yardstick

yellow yacht

Write other words that start with this letter.

Zz

Trace and write. Circle your best Z or z on each line.

Z Z Z Z Z Z Z Z Z Z

Z

Zelda

z z z z z z z z z

z

zodiac

zigzag

zany zoologist

Write other words that start with this letter.

Cursive Writing Challenge

Practise writing your signature in cursive.

Cursive Writing Prompts

Write a response to each question.

1. What is your favourite meal of the day? Explain why.

_____

_____

_____

_____

_____

_____

_____

_____

2. Would you rather stay inside or go outside? Explain why.

_____

_____

_____

_____

_____

_____

_____

_____

3. Name someone you admire? Explain why.

_____

_____

_____

_____

_____

_____

_____

_____

Cursive Writing Challenge

Practise your cursive writing. Find a poem you like and copy it using cursive writing.

Exploring Types of Sentences

A **declarative** sentence makes a statement. It ends with a **period**.

Example: Ken went to the park today.

An **interrogative** sentence asks a question. It ends with a **question mark**.

Example: Would you like to go to the park?

An **exclamatory** sentence shows strong feeling, such as excitement, joy, or anger. It ends with an **exclamation mark**.

Examples: I love the park!   Ouch!   I can't wait!

An **imperative** sentence tells someone to do something. It can end with a **period** or with an **exclamation mark**.

Examples: Take off your boots.   Watch out!

---

1. Write two examples of each type of sentence.

a) Declarative:

I had a good day today.

b) Interrogative:

How did you do it like that

c) Exclamatory:

Omg!

d) Imperative:

Go wash t1

Common Nouns vs. Proper Nouns

A **noun** is a word that names a person, place, or thing.

A **common noun** names a person, place, or thing that does not have a specific name. It can be one person, place, or thing, or a **group** of people, places, or things.

A **proper noun** is the **specific name** of a person, place, or thing.

Examples:
The word **city** is a **common noun**, but the city named **Edmonton** is a **proper noun**.

The word **dog** is a **common noun**, but my dog named **Rover** is a **proper noun**.

The word **girl** is a **common noun**, but the girl named **Suzanne** is a **proper noun**.

1. Circle the **common noun**. Underline the **proper noun**. Hint: There can be more than one of each!

   a) The dog barked when the Mike rang the doorbell.

   b) Anna and Cass went for a walk along the beach.

   c) John's mother invited Sammy over for lunch.

   d) Tim had a banana and toast for breakfast today.

   e) Kim's favourite pizza toppings are pepperoni, cheese, and green peppers.

2. Circle whether the word is a **common noun** or a **proper noun**.

   a) pants   common noun   proper noun

   b) Sheila   common noun   proper noun

   c) dishwasher   common noun   proper noun

   d) Quebec   common noun   proper noun

Abstract Nouns

An **abstract noun** is a word that names an idea that is used as the subject of a sentence.

An **idea** is something that you cannot touch, see, taste, smell, or hear.

Example: Gene's **honesty** *helped him make the right decision when he found someone's wallet.*

In this example, **honesty** is the subject of the sentence. That makes it a noun.

Honesty is an idea that we cannot see, hear, touch, smell, or taste, so it is an abstract noun.

Other examples of abstract nouns are *kindness*, *sorrow*, *strength*, and *confusion*.

1. Read the sentence. Highlight the **subject** of the sentence, then choose whether it is an **abstract noun** or a **common noun**.

   a) The soldier's courage helped him in battle.   common noun   ~~abstract noun~~

   b) The dog played catch.   ~~common noun~~   abstract noun

   c) Sonia's imagination was very powerful.   common noun   ~~abstract noun~~

   d) Trust is very important in a friendship.   common noun   ~~abstract noun~~

2. Use these abstract nouns in a sentence.

   a) hope

   I hope we Play tommorw

   b) talent

   That girl has so talent

   c) health

   is your health ok

Collective Nouns

A **collective noun** is a group of nouns that, when referred to together, become one.
*Example: Five students can come together to be one **group** of students.*

It is important to think of a collective noun as one group because, when using the collective noun in a sentence, you write the verb using the **he**, **she**, or **it** formation.

*Examples: Five students **walk** to school.*
*A group of students **walks** to school.*

---

1. Mark each **collective noun** in each sentence.

   a) A pack of wolves raced through the forest.

   b) Do you have a deck of cards?

   c) The flock of sheep quietly ate grass.

   d) There was a crowd waiting for the gates to open.

   e) The team did very well at the tournament.

   f) There is a beautiful bouquet of roses on the table.

   g) The troupe of actors performed the play outdoors.

2. Use the following collective nouns in a sentence.

   a) herd

   The heard os sheep were being fed grass

   b) collection

   I have a rock collection

Plural Nouns Review

Remember, when making nouns plural, you need to:

• Add **s** to make most nouns plural.

• Add **es** to nouns that end in **s**, **sh**, **ch**, or **x**.

• For nouns ending in a **consonant + y**, change **y** to **i** and add **es**.

• For nouns ending in a **vowel + y**, add **s**.

Watch out for tricky plurals!

• For plural nouns ending in **o**, add **s** or **es**.

• Some nouns change the word to make it plural.

Examples: children   feet   calves   lives   sheep

---

2. Write the plural of the noun.

a) half ___halves___

b) tooth ___teeth___

c) foot ___feet___

d) ability ___abilities___

e) life ___lives___

f) toy ___toys___

g) door ___doors___

h) woman ___weman___

i) wife ___wives___

j) class ___classes___

k) sheep ___sheep___

l) wish ___wishes___

m) quiz ___quizes___

n) loaf ___loaves___

o) berry ___berries___

p) dish ___dishes___

q) witch ___witches___

r) fox ___foxes___

s) mouse ___mice___

t) stitch ___stitches___

Pronouns

A **pronoun** is a word that takes the place of a **noun**.
Use pronouns to avoid repetition in your writing.

A **subject pronoun** is used to take the place of nouns that name **people**, **places**, or **things** that are the **subject** of a sentence. That means that the noun that is being replaced is <u>doing</u> an action.

Subject pronouns are **I**, **you**, **he**, **she**, **we**, **they**, and **it**.

---

1. Fill in the blank with the correct **subject pronoun** that takes the place of the noun in brackets.

a) ___She___ is a good swimmer. (Marie)

b) ___We___ went for a walk. (Raj and I)

c) My name is Mona. ___I___ just finished grade 4. (Mona)

d) Hey Alex! Do ___you___ want to come to the park with me? (Alex)

e) ___they___ did their homework together. (Sandra and Cathy)

f) Cara is happy ___she___ is starting school next week. (Cara)

g) Mark is excited. ___he___ got a new a bike for his birthday. (Mark)

h) I had ice cream for a treat and ___it___ was delicious. (the ice cream)

i) There is a new type of notebook at the store. I want to buy two of ___them___ after school tonight. (notebooks)

j) My grandmother gave me two new blankets for my birthday. ___they___ are very nice and warm. (the blankets)

Object Pronouns

A **pronoun** is a word that replaces a **noun**.
Use pronouns to avoid repetition in your writing.

An **object pronoun** is used to take the place of nouns that name **people**, **places**, or **things** that are the **object** of a sentence. That means that the noun that is being replaced is <u>receiving</u> an action.

Object pronouns are *me*, *you*, *her*, *him*, *it*, *us*, and *them*.

1. Fill in the blank to replace the noun in the brackets with the appropriate **object pronoun**.

a) Alethea gave her snack to ___her___ . (Piya)

b) My mother packed ___it___ in my lunch. (a banana)

c) My name is Amy. The babysitter walked ___me___ and my brother home. (Amy)

d) My sister watched ___us___ while my parents were out. (my friend and me)

e) The teacher dismissed ___us___ early on Friday. (our class)

f) Rodney's friend made ___him___ a sandwich. (Rodney)

g) My friends played with ___them___ . (my brother's friends)

h) I loaned ___it___ to my aunt. (a book)

i) Hey Ken, do ___you___ want to go to the movies on Saturday? (Ken)

j) I went to the library with ___them___ after school. (Kathy and Alex)

k) Ben and I ate ___it___ for lunch today. (the pizza)

Pronouns: *Me* vs. *I*

Me and **I** are both pronouns that you can use to replace your own name.

Use *I* when you are the subject of the sentence. That means you are the person doing an action to or with someone else.

Example: I walked beside you.

Use *me* when someone is doing an action to or with you. This means you are the object of the sentence.

*Example: You walked beside **me**.*

Tip: If you are unsure whether to use **me** or **I**, take the other person and the word "and" out of the sentence and read it again with the word you chose.

Example: Tony and me went to the store.
Me went to the store. (incorrect)   *Tony and I went to the store.* (correct!)

---

1. Fill in the blank with either *me* or *I*.

a) ___I___ want pizza for lunch.

b) John likes ___Me___.

c) You and ___I___ played soccer yesterday.

d) Sandy is going to invite you and ___I___ to her party.

e) ___I___ borrowed three books from the library.

f) Tessa is going to the movies with ___Me___ tomorrow.

g) There are three flies sitting on ___me___.

h) This is what ___I___ want for my birthday.

i) This summer is too hot for ___Me___.

j) Matt asked if you and ___I___ want to go swimming tomorrow.

Indefinite Pronouns: *Someone* and *Nobody*

A **pronoun** is a word that replaces a **noun**.
Use pronouns to avoid repetition in your writing.

An **indefinite pronoun** is used when the noun being replaced is not certain.
Example: I invited four people to my birthday party. **Nobody** *has replied yet.*

Nobody is an **indefinite pronoun**. This is because **nobody** can replace any one of the four people invited to the party, but it does not say specifically which person.

Someone and *nobody* are **common indefinite pronouns**.

1. Fill in the blank with **someone** or **nobody**. Use the **indefinite pronoun** that fits best.

a) I did not know we had a test today. _____ told me about it.

b) _____ left the water running. Now the backyard is flooded.

c) _____ gave me a gift for my birthday. I do not know who it was.

d) There was so much ice cream at the party, _____ could ever finish it all.

e) I would like it if _____ would take me to the toy store this weekend.

f) I made a mess all by myself. _____ else should have to help me clean it up.

g) Jennifer was lost. She hoped _____ could help her find her way.

h) _____ understood the math problems. So the teacher gave us more time to learn.

i) I know _____ who does not like cats.

l) _____ can help me with my homework. It's too hard!

Subordinate Clauses: What Are They?

A **subordinate clause** is an incomplete thought (sentence fragment) that leaves the reader asking "What happened next?" A subordinate clause depends on a complete thought (complete sentence) to make sense. This complete thought is called the **main clause**.

A **main clause** contains a **subject** and a **verb**. A **subordinate clause** also contains a subject and verb, but is an incomplete thought. It makes the most sense when it is paired with the **main clause** of the sentence.

Example:
He played in the school band. (main clause) *Because he loved music.* (subordinate clause)

Both clauses can come together to make a **complex sentence** that makes more sense.

Example:
He played in the school band because he loved music.

---

1. Rewrite the **main clause** and the **subordinate clause** into a **complex sentence**.

a) I will take out the garbage. If you come to the park with me.

_____

b) I got the best seat. Because I got there first.

_____

c) We will go to the movies. When my aunt comes over.

_____

d) I will fail my test. If I do not study.

_____

e) My dad will let me play outside. After I do my chores.

_____

f) I can play with my puppy. When I finish my homework.

_____

Subordinate Conjunctions

A **subordinate conjunction** is used at the beginning of a **subordinate clause** to join it to the main clause. A **subordinate clause** relates and joins two separate thoughts.

Some common **subordinate conjunctions** are *because*, *if*, *once*, *since*, *unless*, *until*, *when*, and *while*.

---

1. Use the **subordinate conjunction** that fits best to join together the two clauses.

a) I will walk the dog. I get home from school.

<u>once</u>

b) I cannot go out for recess. I finish the assignment.

<u>until</u>

c) I will not get a good mark. I study for my test.

<u>unless</u>

d) I had to walk to school. I missed the bus.

<u>because</u>

e) I bought an ice cream cone. I was at the mall.

<u>when</u>

f) My sister listened to music. She painted her toenails.

<u>while</u>

g) Ana feels better. Her cold ended.

<u>since</u>

h) We are going to the cottage. My uncle arrives.

<u>If</u>

Adverbs: Adverbial Phrases

An **adverb** is used to describe an **action**.

You describe an action by modifying **when**, **where**, or **how something is happening**.

Example: I will do my homework tomorrow.

An **adverbial phrase** is an adverb that consists of more than one word.

*Example: I will do my homework **in an hour.***

An adverbial phrase is when a small group of words works together to change **when**, **where**, or **how an action is happening**.

In the sentence above, ***in an hour*** tells you when an action will be completed. This means that it acts like an adverb. But it is not a true adverb because, on their own, these words do not describe an action. But when they work together, they have the same function as an adverb.

---

1. Identify the **adverbs**. Colour them green. Identify the **adverbial phrases**. Colour them blue.

as soon as	in the cupboard	below	in an hour	with ease
now	cheerfully	soon	better	brightly
in a minute	south	in the classroom	yesterday	quickly
fast	a day ago	easily	never	more
above	with difficulty	neatly	occasionally	north

Verbs: Past, Present, and Future Tenses

A **verb** is a word for an action or a feeling.

Use different tenses to talk about actions that **have happened**, **are happening**, or **will happen**.

The **past tense** is used for an action that has **already happened**.
*Examples: I **walked** to the store last night.   Tom walked to the store yesterday.*

The **future tense** is used for an action that **will happen soon**.
*Examples: I **will walk** to the store after school.   Tom will walk to the store after work.*

The **present tense** is used for an action that is **currently happening** or is **continuously happening**.
*Examples: I **walk** to the store after school every day.   Tom walks to the store every day.*

---

1. Fill in the blank with the correct form of verb in brackets. Identify whether you used the **past**, **present**, or **future tense**. The first one is done for you.

   a) My sister ___walks___ to the store every night. (walking)

      My sister <u>walks</u> to the store every night.   **present tense**

   b) My mom ___Sang___ in the shower two days ago. (singing)

      _____

   c) My teacher ___will give___ a test in two weeks. (giving)

      _____

   d) Jessica ___talked___ about a book last week. (talking)

      _____

   e) Kwame ___eats___ a sandwich every day for lunch. (eating)

      _____

© Chalkboard Publishing

Exploring Commas

A **comma** is a type of punctuation mark.

Use a **comma** to tell a reader to pause between the words it separates.

Example: Please get a book, sit quietly, and read.

Use **commas** to separate three or more words in a series.

Commas separate **subjects**, **predicates**, and **adjectives** in a series.

Example: My favourite colours are red, blue, green, and yellow.

Important: **Do not** use a comma **after the last word in a series**.

1. Rewrite each sentence using the **commas** correctly.

a) I made a salad with lettuce cucumber and tomato.

_____

b) There is milk cheese and bread in the refrigerator.

_____

c) My teacher gave us math reading writing and science for homework.

_____

d) June July August and September are my favourite months.

_____

e) There were monkeys giraffes elephants and jaguars at the zoo.

_____

Reading Comprehension Tips

Reading comprehension is the cornerstone of a child's academic success. By completing the activities in this book, children will develop and reinforce essential reading comprehension skills. Children will benefit from a wide variety of opportunities to practise engaging with text as active readers who can self-monitor their understanding of what they have read.

Children will focus on the following:

Identifying the Purpose of the Text
- The reader understands, and can tell you, why they read the text.

Understanding the Text
- What is the main idea of the text?
- What are the supporting details?
- Which parts are facts and which parts are opinions?

Analyzing the Text
- How does the reader's background knowledge enhance the text clues to help the reader answer questions about the text or draw conclusions?
- What inferences can be made by using information from the text, combined with what the reader already knows?
- How does the information from the text help the reader make predictions?
- What is the cause and effect between events?

Making Connections
How does the topic or information being read remind the reader of what they already know?
- Text-to-self connections: How does this text relate to your own life?
- Text-to-text connections: Have I read something like this before? How is this text similar to something I have read before? How is this text different from something I have read before?
- Text-to-world connections: What does this text remind you of in the real world?

Using Text Features
- How do different text features help the reader?

Text Features

Text features help the reader to understand the text better. Here is a list of text features with a brief explanation of how they help the reader.

Contents	Here the reader will find the title of each section, what page each text starts on within sections, and where to find specific information.
Chapter Title	The chapter title gives the reader an idea of what the text will be about. The chapter title is often followed by subheadings within the text.
Title and Subheading	The title or topic is found at the top of the page. The subheading is right above a paragraph. There may be more than one subheading in a text.
Map	Maps help the reader understand where something is happening. It is a visual representation of a location.
Diagram and Illustration	Diagrams and illustrations give the reader additional visual information about the text.
Label	A label tells the reader the title of a map, diagram, or illustration. Labels also draw attention to specific elements within a visual.
Caption	Captions are words that are placed underneath the visuals. Captions give the reader more information about the map, diagram, or illustration.
Fact Box	A fact box tells the reader extra information about the topic.
Table	A table presents text information in columns and rows in a concise and often comparative way.
Bold and Italic Text	**Bold** and *italic* text are used to emphasize a word or words, and signify that this is important vocabulary.

Making Connections with What I Have Read

After reading...	It reminds me of...	This helps me make a connection to...
		☐ something else I have read ☐ myself ☐ the world around me
		☐ something else I have read ☐ myself ☐ the world around me
		☐ something else I have read ☐ myself ☐ the world around me
		☐ something else I have read ☐ myself ☐ the world around me

The Wise Chief and His Wife (Based on a folktale from Africa)

There was once a village with a very wise chief. All the people in the village brought their problems to him. This pleased the chief greatly. He was proud that the villagers respected his wisdom.

One day, an old man came to see the chief. "My four goats have been stolen!" he cried. "I am sure my neighbour did it. Please help me."

The chief sent for the neighbour. When he arrived, the chief asked him if he had stolen the goats. "Certainly not!" exclaimed the neighbour. "I would never steal."

The chief saw that this would be a difficult problem to solve, but this pleased him. Once again he would use his wisdom to find a solution and, once again, the villagers would be impressed by how wise he was.

The chief thought for a moment and said, "I will give you a question to answer." He turned to the old man. "If you give me the best answer, I will order your neighbour to give you four goats." Then he turned to the neighbour and said, "If you come up with the best answer, you may keep all your goats."

The old man and his neighbour agreed to the chief's plan. "Here is the question," announced the chief. "What is the fastest thing in the world? Do not come back until you have an answer. Do not ask anyone for help." The two men went home, scratching their heads and wondering what the best answer might be.

The old man could not think of an answer, so he asked the question to his daughter Shamika, who was both wise and beautiful. Right away, she came up with an answer. The old man was sure it was the best answer to the question.

The very next morning, the old man went to see the chief. "The question is not that difficult," the old man replied. "Time is the fastest thing in the world. It always goes too fast and we never have enough of it."

"Is this your own answer?" asked the chief. "If you lie, you will be punished."

The old man confessed. "My daughter Shamika helped me. She is very wise."

"Her answer is an excellent one," said the chief. "I would like to meet this daughter who is so very wise."

Soon after, the old man presented Shamika to the chief. The chief was impressed by both her wisdom and her beauty. He asked Shamika to marry him, and she accepted.

"There is one rule," said the chief. "You must not interfere with problems the villagers bring to me." The chief did not want people to think there was anyone in the village as wise as he was. "When we are married, everything in my house will be yours. But if you break this rule, I will send you back to your father." Shamika agreed, and soon after the two were married.

Before long, two boys in the village came to the chief with a problem. Each boy claimed that the other had stolen one of his sheep. Shamika could tell right away which boy was lying, but she said nothing. The chief gave them a question to answer, and sent them home to think. Shamika went to the boy who had told the truth and gave him an answer to the chief's question, even though she knew she should not.

The next morning, the boy told the chief the answer Shamika had given him. "Is this your own answer?" asked the chief. "If it is not, I will punish you."

The boy admitted that he had learned the answer from Shamika. The chief was furious. "I told you all that I have is yours," he said to Shamika, "yet you broke the one rule I gave you. You must return to your father's house."

Shamika asked if she could make the chief one final meal. "Fine," said the chief. "Then take whatever you want and leave my house."

Shamika prepared a huge feast of all the chief's favourite dishes. The chief ate until he could eat no more, and then he fell into a deep sleep.

With the help of some villagers, Shamika carried the sleeping chief to her father's house. When the chief woke, he demanded to know what was going on.

"You said I could take whatever I wanted," said Shamika. "The only thing I wanted was you."

"Where could I find a wife so loving and so wise?" said the chief. "You may return to my home with me. Only a fool would send you away, and I am much too wise to do that."

"The Wise Chief and His Wife"—Think About It!

1. Why was the chief happy when the old man and his neighbour presented him with a difficult problem to solve? Give two reasons.

_____

_____

_____

_____

_____

2. The chief was interested in meeting Shamika because she was wise. Why did the chief not want Shamika to display her wisdom by helping with the problems that the villagers brought to him?

_____

_____

_____

_____

3. a) Why did Shamika give one of the boys an answer to the question the chief asked, when by doing so she was breaking the chief's rule?

_____

_____

_____

b) Think about your answer to the question above. What does it tell you about Shamika?

_____

_____

_____

4. Who do you think is wiser—the chief or Shamika? Explain your answer.

_____

_____

_____

The Magic Mirror (Based on a folktale from Spain)

The king had decided that it was time to find a wife. At the palace, everyone was talking about the news. One of the servants asked, "How will the king choose his bride?"

"The king will not choose his bride," said the king's barber. "I will."

"You, a barber, will choose the king's wife?" the servant asked in disbelief.

"Indeed, it is true," said the barber. "I have told the king that I have in my possession a magic mirror. This mirror can see all the faults in a person's character. If someone has told lies or been unkind to others, the mirror can tell. If someone is greedy or too proud, the mirror can tell. It is impossible to hide anything from the mirror. For every fault, a dark spot appears on the mirror's surface. The king has agreed that I should use this mirror to choose a wife for him. Any woman who wishes to marry the king must look into this mirror while I stand at her side. If no dark spots appear, she will become our queen."

"You are going to be very busy," said the palace cook. "Every unmarried woman in the kingdom will want to look into the mirror."

"Perhaps," said the barber, "but I will work night and day if necessary. Beginning next Monday, women may come to my shop if they are interested in marrying the king. I will have the mirror ready."

Soon, everyone in the kingdom was talking about the barber's magic mirror. When Monday came, a large crowd gathered outside the barber's shop. Everyone wanted to see who came to look into the mirror, but not one woman entered the shop. The same thing happened day after day.

Each day, the king asked the barber if any women had come to look into the mirror. Each day he received the same answer—not one woman had come. The king became very discouraged.

"If I may make a suggestion," the barber told the king, "I have heard of a young woman who is said to have no faults whatsoever. She is highly praised by all who know her, but she is a poor peasant girl who spends her days tending sheep on the hillside. Would you consider marrying such a woman?"

"I would," said the king. "Tell this young woman about the mirror and see if she is willing to look into it. If she is, have her come to the palace. She will look into the mirror in front of the people in my court and anyone else who wishes to attend."

The next day, the barber led the peasant girl into the palace. The royal hall was filled with curious people who wanted to watch the event. The girl was very shy, as she had never dreamed of meeting the king, let alone marrying him. The king found her quite charming.

Has the barber explained to you about the mirror?" the king asked the girl.

"Yes, Your Majesty," she replied.

"You understand that if there are any faults in your character, the mirror will show them?" inquired the king.

"Yes, Your Majesty," answered the girl, blushing. "Everyone makes mistakes now and then, and I am no different. But I love and protect my sheep, and they seem to love me in return. I am not afraid to look into the mirror."

The king motioned to the barber to bring the mirror. The hall grew silent. The ladies of the court crowded around the young woman to see what would happen. They were sure she must have some faults. But when she held the mirror and looked into it, not a single dark spot appeared on its surface.

One of the ladies snatched the mirror and passed it around to her friends. No matter who looked into the mirror, no dark spots appeared. "It is a trick!" the ladies cried. "There is no magic in this mirror!" Many were furious that they—or their daughters—had missed a chance to become queen.

The king was not disturbed. "If you had been as confident about your character as this young woman, you would not have been afraid to look into the mirror," he said. "Perhaps there was no magic in the mirror, but it has found me a young woman who is worthy to be my bride."

"Magic Mirror"—Think About It!

1. Before the peasant girl came to the palace, no women wanted to enter the barber's shop to look into the mirror. In your own words, explain why.

_____

_____

_____

_____

2. After the barber described the peasant girl to the king, the barber asked him if he would consider marrying her. Why do you think the barber asked this question, even though people said the girl had "no faults whatsoever"?

_____

_____

_____

_____

3. a) Why do you think the barber lied about the mirror having magic powers?

_____

_____

_____

b) The barber took a big risk by lying about the mirror. What could have gone wrong?

_____

_____

_____

4. The mirror did not have magic powers, so it could not reveal whether the peasant girl had any faults. Why did the king feel confident that the peasant girl was worthy to be his bride?

_____

_____

_____

Tryouts

My name is Nia. I love basketball. We have a basketball hoop in my driveways and if there are no cars, I dribble, position myself properly, and shoot. I have been practicing shooting baskets a lot recently because I want to try out for the basketball team at school. I was getting pretty good at scoring—up to last week.

We were playing a game of basketball in the gym. Everything was going well. I had scored once and my team was winning. Then it happened. I dribbled down the court and—KABOOM!—I collided with a girl from the other team. I felt a sharp pain near my eye. The teacher sent me to the office immediately. The vice-principal took one look at me and handed me a cold compress for my eye.

"You are going to have a shiner," she predicted.

She was right. By the next day I had a black eye. Luckily, that was all I had. My doctor said it could have been worse. The doctor also said that the black eye would heal in a few weeks. The big problem is how do you try out for the basketball team with a black eye?

Some of my classmates teased me at the tryouts but I was determined to make the team. I ignored their teasing and guess what? I am on the team!

Choose a sentence from the text to use as a caption for this illustration.

_____

"Tryouts"—Think About It!

1. From whose point of view is this text told? How do you know?

_____

_____

_____

_____

2. Where does the girl in the story play basketball at home?

_____

3. What is a *compress*?

_____

_____

4. What does the word *shiner* refer to in the text?

_____

_____

5. What does this text remind you of?

_____

_____

_____

_____

6. How does Nia display the character trait *determination*?

_____

_____

_____

_____

Travelling to the Past

The doorbell rang early on the morning of my birthday. I raced to answer the door, but all I could see was a small brown box on my doorstep. The word FRAGILE was plastered across it in giant red letters.

I brought the box inside. My parents were sound asleep, so I grabbed scissors and opened the box carefully. Inside was another box with what looked like a smartphone. There was also a note which read:

Dear Ellen,

Happy birthday! I know you love history and adventure. Follow the instructions and you will have an out-of-this-world adventure. Have the "time" of your life!

Love,
    Cousin Rita

P.S. I know time flies when you are having fun, but remember to always be back in three hours.

It was a time machine! I read the instructions and programmed the time machine to take me to the castle of Queen Elizabeth I, in 1590.

In an instant, I was there and the queen was having dinner.

"Who are you?" Queen Elizabeth asked.

"I am Ellen from far away," I told her.

"Well Ellen from far away, you might as well stay for lunch."

The queen and I discussed explorers, battling the Spanish, and how much fun it is to ride horses.

Then I heard a ding, and I had to return home. I said a hurried goodbye to the queen, and raced to the courtyard

I cannot wait for my next time travel adventure!

"Travelling to the Past"—Think About It!

1. What did the note say in the story?

_____

_____

_____

_____

2. Why did Ellen's cousin send her this kind of present?

_____

_____

_____

_____

3. What time in history did Ellen travel to?

_____

_____

4. What did Ellen and the queen discuss?

_____

_____

5. If you could travel back in time, what time period would you visit, and why?

_____

_____

_____

_____

6. What does the expression "time flies when you are having fun" mean? Use this expression in a sentence.

_____

_____

"Travelling to the Past"—Think About It! (continued)

7. Pretend you have been given a time machine for your birthday. Write a journal entry about your adventure.

Two Friends, Two Places

Hi Sam,

I think it is amazing that we both left Toronto, Ontario, at the same time! It is incredible that we are now living in two different places at the opposite ends of Canada!

Sometimes I feel that my new home in St. John's, Newfoundland, is at the end of the world. I can stand at the top of Signal Hill and gaze out at the Atlantic Ocean. From high up there, you can see the ocean, a few boats, and sometimes icebergs. (When I saw icebergs floating along in the ocean, my jaw dropped!) Sometimes I imagine explorers such as Jacques Cartier travelling for weeks in their small, rusty ships and finally spying this land. (Their jaws must have dropped, too!).

I like St. John's, even though the weather can be cold, damp, and very windy. There have only been two times that I have been able to go up to Signal Hill when the sun was actually shining and I did not feel as though the wind would blow me off into the ocean.

Your friend,
Daniel

Hi Daniel,

It is incredible that we landed at the opposite ends of Canada! It is also amazing that we often have weather like yours here in Vancouver, British Columbia. Sometimes it feels as though it will rain forever. But then, like a miracle, the rain stops and you can see the mountains, the skyscrapers, and the ocean.

Stanley Park is the best park, and I love exploring there. I love walking on the beach and picking up driftwood and rocks, too.

Maybe we can visit each other. I hope so!

Your friend,
Sam

"Two Friends, Two Places"—Think About It!

1. Where are Sam and Daniel both originally from?

_____

_____

2. Where are you from, and have you always lived there?

_____

_____

3. Contrast the weather in St. John's and Vancouver.

_____

_____

_____

4. What can Daniel see from Signal Hill?

_____

5. What does Sam like to do in Stanley Park?

_____

6. What do you enjoy doing in your local park?

_____

_____

_____

7. How did seeing an iceberg make Daniel feel? How would you feel if you saw an iceberg for the first time?

_____

_____

_____

8. What does the expression, "my jaw dropped" mean?

_____

Blog or News?

Is it a blog or is it news? Do you know the difference between a blog and a news report or article? You can find both on many websites, and sometimes they will be about the same subject. Read the following two items that were posted on a book publisher's website:

> *On April 23, the new book by Ana Grimley arrived for sale in bookstores across the country. Her new book is called* The Far Away Country, *a sequel to her first book,* Closer to Home. *The two books are the first in a planned series of four, which together will complete the journey of the book's hero, Justine Waverley. Justine was introduced in* Closer to Home. *In this book, the readers learned about this extraordinary young woman and the problems faced by her family and the town she lived in. In* The Far Away Country, *Justine leaves to find a solution and travels to a place full of danger, but also full of hope.* The Far Away Country *is written for middle readers, ages 9 to 12. This 137-page softcover book has a suggested price of $11.99.*

> *The long-awaited sequel to* Closer to Home *has finally arrived. And it was worth the wait.* The Far Away Country *is even better than the first book. It will keep you glued to the pages, long past the time when you should be asleep. The author, Ana Grimley, has invented a new world so amazing and dazzling, it comes alive in your mind. And Justine once again proves she is no ordinary young woman. This book was written for 9- to 12-year-olds but, like the first book, older kids and even adults will read it and love it. So run, do not walk, to your nearest book store and buy it. You will not be sorry.—Henry Chan*

Can you tell which is the news article and which is the blog? Here are some hints:

• News articles give factual information. They can announce new products or upcoming events. News articles are usually more formal. They should be objective, or, not influenced by personal feelings.

• Blogs give ideas, views, and opinions on something. They may also include factual information, but the focus is on opinion. The writing in blogs is usually more informal. A blog is usually signed by the person who wrote it.

Why is it important to know about different forms of writing? The more you know, the more quickly you can find the information you want. If it is facts you are looking for, check a news article. If you want to know what different people think about something, check a blog.

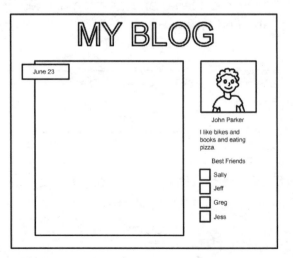

"Blog or News?"——Think About It!

1. What is the main idea of this text? How does the author support this main idea? How does this help you as a reader?

_____

_____

_____

_____

_____

_____

2. Which item is a news article? Use information from the text to support your answer.

_____

_____

_____

_____

_____

_____

3. What is the meaning of the word sequel? Use specific details from the text to support your answer.

_____

_____

_____

4. What is the difference between formal and informal writing?

_____

_____

_____

_____

5. Complete the chart to compare the similarities and differences between the news article and the blog.

News Article	Similarities	Blog

Wayne Gretzky

Wayne Gretzky is one of the most famous Canadian hockey players in North America. Even people who do not follow hockey know who he is. Gretzky played in the National Hockey League (NHL) from 1979 to 1999. He set many records during this time. Many of his records still stand today.

The Great One

Wayne Gretzky's nickname was "The Great One." How did he become so good? Wayne was two and a half when he started skating. A few years later, his father built a rink in their backyard. Wayne would practise four or five hours a day with his brothers. He and his brothers said they learned everything about playing hockey from their dad.

All the practising paid off. Wayne started playing in a hockey league when he was six. By the time he was 13, he had scored 1,000 goals in the league games and tournaments he played.

Wayne was not very big or fast or strong. But he was very smart about hockey. He always seemed to know where the puck was on the ice and what it would do. He would make the right play at the right time. He was not a very fast skater but he was an agile skater. He could change direction in an instant without losing his balance or slowing down. He was a great passer. He would pass the puck to where he thought his teammates would be, not where they were. He was not a selfish player. The most important thing to him was for his team to win. So he would pass the puck to a teammate who had the best chance to score.

Wayne always played his best every game. When he was young, his dad told him he had to perform for the people who were watching. They came to see him play, so he must always be at his best. This was a lesson he never forgot.

After Hockey

After he finished playing hockey, Wayne became involved in many businesses. He donates some of the money he makes to the Wayne Gretzky Foundation. This Foundation helps youngsters all across North America play hockey. Wayne believes that playing hockey helps develop skills that young people need. He also supports many other charities, donating his time and money to help others.

"You miss 100% of the shots you do not take." – Wayne Gretzky

"Wayne Gretzky"—Think About It!

1. Character traits, such as discipline or good sportsmanship, help describe someone's personality. What four character traits did Wayne Gretzky show during his hockey career? Use details from the text to support your choices.

Character Trait	Details from the Text

2. Pretend you are a reporter and you are interviewing Wayne Gretzky. Write down five interview questions you would like to ask him.

_____

_____

_____

_____

_____

_____

"Wayne Gretzky"—Think About It! (continued)

Wayne Gretzky practised four or five hours a day and learned everything he could about hockey from his dad. He was not very big or fast or strong. But he was very smart about hockey and he used that to get better at playing hockey. Wayne showed perseverance to reach his goal of playing in the hockey leagues.

Here are some ways you can show perseverance. Take this survey and think about how you persevere to accomplish your goals.

Perseverance Survey

	Always	Sometimes	Never
I strive to do my best.			
I set a goal and stay focused on it.			
I do not give up if something becomes difficult.			
I do not put off doing things.			
I am self-disciplined.			
I learn from mistakes and failures.			

Do you think you show perseverance? Explain your thinking.

____

____

____

____

Goal Setting

My goal: _____

Why did you choose this goal? _____

List the steps to achieve this goal:

_____

_____

_____

_____

_____

_____

_____

The date you want to achieve your goal by: _____

How will you know if you achieved your goal?

_____

_____

Goal Setting

Stay Safe on the Internet

The Internet is an amazing resource. Many people say that they would have a difficult time living without access to the Internet.

Do you know how to stay safe online? Here are a few tips.

Social Networking and Instant Messaging

Social networking websites and instant messaging (often called IM) can be great ways to keep in touch with friends. But be careful!

- When you set up a personal profile, you may need to give a lot of information about yourself, such as your name, address, email address, telephone number, and more. This information may become available to other people. Before you set up a profile, get a parent or guardian to help you. Make sure to find out who will have access to your personal information, and whether there are ways to keep this information private. Do not include a photograph of yourself in your profile!

- Do not use social networking websites or IM to connect with people you do not know in real life. If you do meet someone new on the Internet, make sure a parent or guardian knows about it. Never arrange to meet a new Internet friend in person, unless a parent or guardian can go with you.

- Be careful what you say in an instant message or on a social networking website. Your comments can be copied and sent to anyone. You might trust the friend you are communicating with, but what happens if you have an argument with your friend or someone steals your friend's laptop or cellphone?

Passwords

Email requires a password. So do many other things people do on the Internet. Keep these password safety tips in mind:

- It is okay to give your passwords to a parent or guardian, but do not share your passwords with anyone else—not even a close friend.

- Choose passwords that are not easy to guess. Create a password from random letters and numbers. You should not use the same password on different websites. So, make sure you write down your passwords and keep them in a safe and private place, or give them to a parent or guardian. Change your passwords regularly.

Email

Email might seem to be a safe way to communicate with people, but you still need to be careful.

- Do not choose an email address that has your full name. Avoid choosing an email address that allows people to guess your full name.

- Remember that an email you send can be forwarded to other people—so be careful what you say.

- Spam is email that is sent to thousands of people who did not ask to receive it. Spam can be dangerous and can contain viruses that harm your computer. People who want to trick you into giving out your personal information can send it. Before you open an email, check to see who sent it. If you do not know the person, delete the email without opening it.

- If you are getting a lot of spam, ask a parent or guardian to help you learn what you can do about the problem. Remember that if a website asks for your email address before you play a game or do a survey, someone will probably send you spam.

Brain Stretch

On a separate piece of paper, draft a public service announcement that gives Internet safety tips for children. When you are finished, share it with your class. Use this checklist to help you.

- ❏ My public service announcement has a clear message about Internet safety for children.
- ❏ My public service announcement is 15 to 30 seconds long.
- ❏ I created my public service announcement to appeal to my target audience (children or adults).
- ❏ I practised reading my public service announcement with expression.

Adjectives for Writing

Category	Adjectives
Size	big, small, short, tall, fat, skinny, large, medium, slim, thin, slender, tiny, lean, scrawny, huge, gigantic, jumbo, plump, wee, wide, narrow
Shape	round, square, pointed, jagged, oval, chunky, curly, straight, curved, flat, twisted, heart-shaped, spiky, wavy, bent, tangled, messy
Colour	red, orange, yellow, green, blue, purple, pink, grey, white, black, brown, silver, gold
Age	young, old, new, baby, newborn
Sound	loud, quiet, long, short, musical, surprising, soft, noisy, muffled, whispering, growling, grumbling
Light and Brightness	dull, bright, dark, light, clear, flashy, flashing, dim, faint, glowing, flickering, twinkly, twinkling, shiny, shining
Smell	good, bad, strong, sweet, salty, spicy, stinky, sour, delicious, yummy, fresh, rotten, rotting
Feel and Texture	soft, hard, smooth, rough, silky, fluffy, fuzzy, furry, wet, dry, bumpy, lumpy, scratchy, sweaty, slippery, slimy, gritty, dirty, sticky, gummy, jiggly, wiggly, squishy, watery, liquid, solid, rock hard, damp, stiff, firm
Taste	delicious, bitter, sweet, salty, tasty, spicy, yummy, bland, sour, strong
Speed and Movement	quick, quickly, fast, slow, slowly, rapid, rapidly, brisk, briskly, swift, swiftly, instant, instantly, late
Temperature	hot, cold, icy, frosty, chilly, burning, boiling, steamy, sizzling, cool, warm, freezing, frozen, damp, humid, melting

Alliteration

Alliteration is the repetition of the same letters or sounds at the start of two or more words in a sentence.

Example: Alfred alligator always acts annoyingly.

Create some of your own examples of **alliteration** below.

1 _____

2 _____

3 _____

4 _____

5 _____

6 _____

7 _____

8 _____

9 _____

10 _____

Sensational Similes

A **simile** is a phrase that contains the word **like** or **as** to make a comparison between two different things.

Example: David was as hungry as a bear!

Write some of your own **similes**.

1 _____

2 _____

3 _____

4 _____

5 _____

6 _____

7 _____

8 _____

9 _____

10 _____

Hyperboles

Hyperboles are exaggerated statements used to stress an idea.

Examples:

My backpack weighs a ton!

I am so hungry I could eat horse!

The chef made enough food to feed an army!

1. Write some of your own **hyperboles**.

   a) _____

   b) _____

   c) _____

   d) _____

   e) _____

   f) _____

BRAIN STRETCH

Write a paragraph about getting ready for a trip. Include at least four hyperboles.

_____

_____

_____

_____

Idioms

Idioms are common expressions understood by people to mean something different than their literal meaning.

Write a sentence using each of these idioms to show the meaning.

1. be in hot water _____

2. get cold feet _____

3. a basket case _____

4. I'm all ears _____

5. a rip-off _____

6. goose is cooked _____

7. pig out _____

8. let the cat out of the bag _____

BRAIN STRETCH

List other examples of idioms you know.

_____

_____

_____

Cinquain Poem

A **cinquain** is a poem that has five lines.

Use the lines below to write cinquain poems about different subjects.

FORMAT

Line 1: two syllables

Line 2: four syllables

Line 3: six syllables

Line 4: eight syllables

Line 5: two syllables

FORMAT

Line 1: two syllables

Line 2: four syllables

Line 3: six syllables

Line 4: eight syllables

Line 5: two syllables

Haiku Poem

Haiku is a traditional style of Japanese poetry. Usually, haiku poems have a nature theme, such as animals or the seasons. Haiku poems are a good way to describe something.

Haiku poems have only three lines. There are five syllables in its first line, seven syllables in its second line, and five syllables in its third line. The third line is usually a subject that is only slightly connected to the first two lines.

Leaves blow in the wind
Skies darken and thunder booms.
The rain helps things grow.

Write your own **haiku**.

1. Choose a subject for your haiku. Brainstorm a list of words about your subject. Beside each word, note how many syllables it has.

2. Choose a second subject for the last line of your haiku. It should remind the reader of the subject.

_____

3. Write your haiku.

Line 1 (5 syllables) _____

Line 2 (7 syllables) _____

Line 3 (5 syllables) _____

Limericks

If you have a poem that is funny and just five lines long, it is likely a **limerick**.

The first, second, and fifth lines rhyme in this style of poem and each line is either eight syllables long or nine syllables long.

A limerick's third and fourth lines rhyme, and each line is either five syllables long or six syllables long.

These little poems are usually silly or about something funny. No one knows for sure where the name *limerick* comes from, but it may have something to do with the town of Limerick in Ireland.

> There was a young boy who one night
> Decided a limerick to write.
> It took him some time,
> To make it all rhyme,
> But finally he got it just right!

Write your own **limerick**.

☐ Choose a subject for your limerick—something funny works well.

☐ Check that the first, second, and fifth lines rhyme.

☐ Make sure the first, second, and fifth lines are all eight or nine syllables long.

☐ Make sure the third and fourth lines rhyme with each other.

☐ Check that the third and fourth lines are both five or six syllables long.

Write your own limerick.

Line 1 _____

Line 2 _____

Line 3 _____

Line 4 _____

Line 5 _____

Persuasive Text

When you try to persuade a reader to do something, or to convince them that they should agree with your opinion, you are writing **persuasive text**. Advertisements are persuasive texts and so are essays, movie reviews, complaint letters, and more. This style of writing is non-fiction, and it uses uses facts and true stories to build a strong position. Persuasive text begins with a clear statement of how you feel about a subject, then uses strong examples that build on each other. It ends with a summary of the facts, and repeats the purpose of the text.

Persuasive Text Checklist

☐ Open with a strong statement of the purpose of your writing and what your opinion is.

☐ Use mostly the present tense.

☐ Use facts and examples, perhaps in a list, to support your idea.

☐ Use active verbs and strong adjectives to involve and convince the reader.

☐ Try using repeated words, exclamation marks, and humour to persuade your reader.

☐ Check that your piece is clearly organized and that your facts build on each other. You can use words that help connect ideas, such as "however," "therefore," or "because."

☐ If you like, include arguments that go against your points, to show that you have looked at both sides of the argument.

☐ Finish with a summary of your points and repeat your opening statement, using slightly different wording.

Narrative Text

Narrative text is a type of writing that either reports on the events of a real-life story or tells a make-believe story.

A narrative text is usually written in the past tense and in the third person, and it focuses on the experiences of the characters. It is usually a straight-forward story that may have a personal meaning for the writer, or may give readers insights into their own lives.

Examples: legend, folktale, tall tale, story, song, or *poem*

A **personal narrative** is a true story that happened to the writer.

Examples: autobiography, diary entry, journal, log, blog entry, or *personal experience*

Narrative Text Checklist

☐ Decide whether you are going to write in the first person (I, we) or third person (he, she, they).

☐ Begin by setting the scene and introducing your characters.

☐ Choose what the problem or conflict in your story will be.

☐ Brainstorm how the main characters will solve the problem.

☐ Decide whether your story will have a happy or sad ending.

☐ If you like, end your story with a moral, a message, or a description of how your characters have been affected by dealing with the problem or crisis.

☐ Use active verbs, and strong adjectives and adverbs.

☐ Write dialogue that helps break up the text and moves your story along.

☐ Review your tale to make sure it will amuse or entertain your reader and tell a good story.

Procedural Text

Text that gives instructions about how to do something is called **procedural text**. This could be recipes, experiments, an instructional manual, rules for a game, instructions for a craft, or a list of steps for safety or success.

Procedural text often has subheadings. For example, a recipe might have subheadings such as ingredients, directions, and serving suggestions.

The writing in procedural text should be clear, direct, and detailed.

Procedural Text Checklist

☐ Decide what you are going to tell your reader to do. What do you want to achieve?

☐ Think about who your target audience is. For whom are you writing these instructions?

☐ Write in the present tense. Use action words.

☐ After you have written your text, review it to make sure your instructions are clear and in the correct order.

☐ Decide whether you should add subheadings. How many? Where should you place them?

☐ Consider numbering your steps—would that help your reader to follow them?

☐ Review your text to make sure you have included enough information on how, where, and when the reader is to complete each step.

☐ Read your text again and decide whether you should add more details.

Expository Text

Expository text informs a reader or exposes the reader to facts. It is a form of non-fiction writing, which means it tells about real situations and topics. Readers can learn from it and find out explanations for events or actions. Textbooks, news articles, language books, self-help books, brochures, and catalogues are all types of expository text. This type of writing is clear and organized, and may include lists, diagrams, maps, and more.

Expository Text Checklist

☐ Choose a topic to tell your reader about. Get to the point quickly.

☐ Pick the facts that you are going to use in your text. Arrange them so they are easy to understand.

☐ Decide whether your text would be better if you included drawings, photos, maps, or lists.

☐ If you like, try asking a question, then providing an answer.

☐ You can also get across information by comparing and contrasting events, topics, or objects.

☐ Try describing an action (a cause), then include several events that are the effect of that cause.

☐ Review your writing to make sure it is clear and easy to understand

☐ At the end of your expository text, tell the reader why the information is important.

Fact or Opinion?

- **Facts** are things that can be proven to be true.
- **Opinions** are views or judgements based on something a person thinks or believes.

Read a newspaper story and complete the chart. Title _____

Piece of Information	Fact or Opinion?	How do you know?

Write a Review

Share your opinion about a book, play, or movie.

Title of Media: _____

Type of Media: _____

Outline of the Main Idea:

_____

_____

_____

In My Opinion:

_____

_____

_____

_____

_____

_____

_____

_____

_____

_____

_____

☐ **Recommended**

☐ **Not recommended**

Reviewed by:

_____

My Brilliant Board Game

Create your own board game! Base your game on a theme that you are studying in class or something that interests you.

What You Need

- a base for the game board, such as a large piece of construction paper, a clean takeout pizza box, or file folder
- colouring materials
- scissors
- glue
- construction paper
- 2 numbered cubes

What You Do

1. Choose a theme for your game.

2. Create a path the game pieces will follow. You may choose to give your path a specific shape: a U-shape, an L-shape, a square, or an oval. Make your path at least 50 squares long.

3. Add spaces where you have to stack question cards cut from heavy paper. Print or handwrite questions on the cards.

4. Test the game to see if it is too hard or has enough spaces.

5. Cut small figures out of paper to use as game pieces, or use materials that are available.

6. Decorate your game board to make it colourful and eye-catching.

7. Write rules and directions on how to play your game.

Rules and How to Play

- How does a player move around the board? Here are some ideas:
  - roll the numbered cubes
  - pick up a card and answer a question
  - follow the instructions on the game board spaces
- How many people can play?
- Are there penalties for wrong answers?

Ideas for Game Cards

- math questions
- true or false questions
- questions requiring answers
- multiple choice questions

"My Brilliant Board Game"—Think About It!

1. What is your board game called?

_____

2. What is the theme of your game?

_____

_____

_____

3. How many players are there?

_____

4. How does someone win the game?

_____

_____

_____

5. What are the rules, and how do you play?

_____

_____

_____

_____

_____

_____

Canada's National Symbols

Around the world, the beaver and the maple leaf are *emblems* of Canada. But how did these symbols come to represent our country?

Mmmm, Maple Syrup!

As early as 1700, people began to use the maple leaf as a symbol of Canada. The country's Aboriginal peoples taught early European explorers and settlers how to make sweet syrup from the maple tree sap.

By the mid-1800s, Canada's soldiers were using the maple leaf in their badges. When Canada became a country in 1867, composer Alexander Muir wrote the song "The Maple Leaf Forever." For several decades, it was considered Canada's national song.

More Maple Leaves

When Canada still used pennies, that coin had maple leaves on it. But between 1876 and 1901, the maple leaf appeared on all Canadian coins.

In World War I and World War II, Canada's fighters wanted a symbol that would remind them of their country, and would show they were different from any other soldiers. They picked the maple leaf.

It was likely that when Canada chose its current red-and-white flag in 1965, people around the world recognized that a maple leaf "means" Canada. The red maple leaf in the middle of the flag is a bold, distinct symbol.

Fur Hats

Canada might never have been explored and settled by Europeans if it had not been for the beaver. In the late 1600s and early 1700s, many men in Europe wore top hats. Those hats were made from fur, and Europeans quickly realized that beaver fur was perfect for the job.

Today you know the Hudson's Bay Company as a department store, but it was originally a fur trading company. In 1678, the company put on its coat of arms not just one beaver, but four of them. This shows how important the animal was to the company.

Stamps, Coins, and More

Canada's first postage stamp featured a beaver. Since the stamp cost 3 cents, it became known as the "Three Penny Beaver." For many years, the Canadian nickel has also had a beaver on it.

One of the country's most famous planes is the de Havilland Beaver. It can land on land, water, or snow, and makes travel to Canada's wilderness possible.

At outdoor festivals, especially in the winter, be sure to try the sweet treat known as a Beaver Tail. This pastry is shaped like a beaver's tail and is delicious!

Other Symbols

When people in other countries think of Canada, they likely think of snow! Other things that make people think of Canada are fishing boats, hockey, and the Calgary Stampede. Toques, lacrosse, and snowmobiles are other symbols of the country.

More modern symbols of Canada include Toronto's CN Tower and the space shuttle component called the Canadarm.

BRAIN STRETCH

List five reasons why the people of Canada should be proud to be Canadian.

1

2

3

4

5

"Canada's National Symbols"—Think About It!

1. Use the clues from the text to explain what *emblem* means.

   _____

2. Why did the maple leaf become a symbol of Canada?

   _____

   _____

3. Why do you think soldiers fighting in World War I and World War II wanted a badge that reminded them of their home country?

   _____

   _____

   _____

4. When was Canada's red-and-white flag designed?

   _____

5. What was featured on Canada's first postage stamp? What was this stamp known as?

   _____

   _____

   _____

6. Choose one of the symbols mentioned in this text. Write a paragraph about why you think it is an important Canadian symbol.

   _____

   _____

   _____

   _____

   _____

   _____

   _____

   _____

7. Design a new Canadian stamp.

Describe what symbols of Canada you used in your stamp and why you chose them.

_____

_____

_____

_____

The Musical Ride

One of the most famous symbols of Canada is the Royal Canadian Mounted Police (RCMP), in their red jackets and brown Stetson hats. A specially trained group of RCMP officers, or Mounties, perform intricate manoeuvres on horseback in a spectacle known as the Musical Ride.

The Ride Begins

In 1867, Canada had just become its own country and it was growing and changing quickly. The country's first prime minister, John A. Macdonald, was worried about keeping law and order in such a huge area. So in 1873, Canada's government set up the North-West Mounted Police (NWMP). They were police officers who enforced the country's laws, while on horseback.

Early members of the North-West Mounted Police (NWMP) wanted to show off their riding skills. So the officers practised cavalry drill manoeuvers choreographed to music. They called it the Musical Ride and, in 1904, they gave the first public performances in Manitoba and Saskatchewan. When the police force became the RCMP, in 1920, the tradition of the Musical Ride continued.

The Musical Ride Today

Each year, about 800 RCMP officers apply to take part in the Musical Ride, but only 12 to 15 are chosen. Although women were admitted to the force only in 1974, many of the officers in the Musical Ride are women.

It takes about 16 weeks of grueling practice for the 32 riders and their horses to put together a Musical Ride show. They must learn many patterns and figures, with names such as the Bridal Arch, the Wagon Wheel, Thread the Needle, and the Dome.

The Musical Ride Horses

The horses are perhaps more important than the officers in the Musical Ride. They must be good-natured and able to cope well with constantly changing sights and sounds. Elegant and athletic, they must also be able to work extremely close together. All horses in the Musical Ride are black because they look so impressive with the Mounties' red coats.

When the horses are three years old, they begin training to deal with parades, traffic, and crowds. At age 6, they begin special Musical Ride training, and some horses perform with the Ride until they are more than 20 years old.

Just before the performance, each rider takes a wet brush and stencil and marks a maple leaf on their horse's rump. Every Musical Ride ends with the horses and riders charging down the field—a dramatic end to an event that is a unique part of Canadian history.

"The Musical Ride"—Think About It!

1. What is the Musical Ride?

   _____

   _____

2. List three characteristics of Musical Ride horses. Give a reason for each choice.

Characteristic	Reason

3. How many RCMP officers who apply to take part in the Musical Ride are turned down each year?

   _____

   _____

4. How many weeks of practice does it take to put a Musical Ride show together?

   _____

   _____

5. What are the names of some of the manoeuvres the horses and riders have to learn?

   _____

   _____

6. Right before each performance, the riders do something special with their horses. What do they do?

   _____

Create a Musical Ride Advertisement

Encourage people to come to see the Musical Ride. Design a print advertisement for the Musical Ride. Use the tips shown below to design your print advertisement.

1. Include a memorable headline:

Create a catchy phrase that will help people remember your message. For example, "Ocean Cruises—this is the life!"

2. Graphics should be eye-catching:

Choose graphics that will help communicate your message. For example, a picture of the ocean will create an impression of peacefulness. The colours you choose are important too!

Ocean Cruises—this is the life!

All of the top celebrities choose our cruises!

Book Now! Get 40% Off!

3. Carefully plan the text:

The type and size of font you choose will help communicate your message. Plan the location of the words on the paper carefully so that people will read it.

4. Include an attractive logo:

Craft a visual sign or symbol to represent the manufacturer or group. For example, a ship with a wave under it could be used to represent a cruise line.

5. Use the whole space to your advantage:

Make sure every part of the ad space helps people focus on your message. Blank areas are fine.

The Great Lakes

No wonder these lakes in northeastern North America have received the name the Great Lakes. They are the largest group of freshwater lakes on Earth!

The Five Lakes

The five great lakes are located along the border between Canada and the United States. The lakes border on the province of Ontario, as well as on the American states of Illinois, Indiana, Minnesota, Michigan, New York, Ohio, Pennsylvania, and Wisconsin.

It is easy to remember the names of all five lakes. Just remember the word HOMES and it will remind you of the first letter in each of the names of the lakes: Huron, Ontario, Michigan, Erie, Superior.

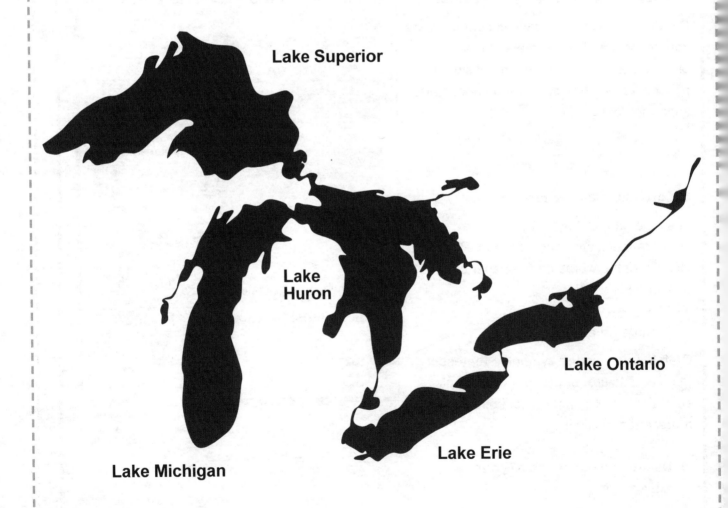

Great Water, Shining Water

The largest Great Lake is Lake Superior. It is the largest inland lake anywhere on Earth. Its name comes from the fact that it lies above, or superior to, the other Great Lakes. Aboriginal peoples called it *Gitchigumi* (pronounced *Git-chee-goo-mee*), which means "great lake."

Lake Michigan lies entirely within the United States and is the world's largest lake that is completely within one country. The lake's name comes from the Aboriginal word *mishigami* (pronounced *mih-shi-ga-mee*), which means "great water."

Lake Huron was named by French explorers for the Huron Aboriginal peoples who lived in the area. A neighbouring Aboriginal group also gave its name to Lake Erie. Lake Ontario gets its name from an Aboriginal word that means "shining water."

Between the Lakes

Between Lake Huron and Lake Erie is Lake St. Clair. It is so much smaller than the lakes around it that it is not considered one of the Great Lakes. Between Lake Erie and Lake Ontario is Niagara Falls, one of North America's largest waterfalls.

Ships moving grain and other supplies from Canada's prairies to countries in Europe are loaded in Thunder Bay, up on Lake Superior. They travel across Lake Superior, Lake Huron, and Lake Erie, but they have to bypass Niagara Falls by sailing through the Welland Canal. They finish their trip by sailing the length of Lake Ontario, then down the St. Lawrence River to the Atlantic Ocean.

Stormy Lakes

Because the Great Lakes are so large, they are known for their rolling waves, blustery winds, and strong currents. Storms on these waters can be very dangerous. In the fall, bad weather can blow up suddenly. There are also hidden reefs in the Great Lakes that can wreck a ship.

Hundreds of ocean-going vessels have been shipwrecked in the Great Lakes. Most of them lie deep below the dark waters of Lake Huron, where the eastbound and westbound shipping lanes cross. There is also an area farther up in Lake Superior that has become known as the "Graveyard of the Great Lakes."

"The Great Lakes"—Think About It!

1. What is the acronym that can be used to help remember the names of the great lakes? What are the lakes' names?

_____

_____

_____

_____

2. Which of the great lakes is that largest?

_____

3. How did Lake Huron get its name?

_____

_____

4. What route must a ship carrying grain or other supplies from the prairies take if it is heading for Europe?

_____

_____

_____

5. In which Great Lake are most of the ships that have sunk? What is the nickname of one of those places?

_____

_____

6. Which three Great Lakes have Aboriginal names? What are the names and what do they mean?

_____

_____

_____

7. Where did the other two Great Lakes get their names? Explain.

_____

_____

_____

Black Loyalists

In 1775, war broke out in the country now known as the United States. The conflict was between the British and the Americans. The British promised land in Canada to all the black people who fought on their side. These people became known as the Black Loyalists.

Freedom and a Farm

Life was very hard for black people living in the United States in the late 1700s. Many were slaves. Those who were not slaves worried about being sold into slavery by sly traders. All black people faced discrimination because of the colour of their skin. It was difficult for them to find good jobs or places to live.

When the American Revolutionary War broke out between the Americans and the British, many black Americans saw it as an opportunity to make a big change. The British side not only offered them a farm in Canada, but also promised them their freedom.

Heading to Canada

The Black Loyalists stayed loyal to the British side and fought in their army. They battled bravely, but the British side lost. Britain quickly arranged for the Black Loyalists to leave the United States because many were being captured into slavery.

The British gave the Black Loyalists certificates that showed they were free, not slaves. About 3,500 black people sailed north to Canada's Maritimes. Approximately half of the Black Loyalists settled near Shelburne, Nova Scotia.

Birchtown

This settlement in Nova Scotia became known as Birchtown. The name comes from Brigadier General Samuel Birch, a British official. He helped many Loyalists leave the United States.

For the first few years, Birchtown was the largest free African community outside Africa. Today, you can visit the Black Loyalist Heritage Site in Birchtown to find out more about the Black Loyalists.

More Discrimination

Sadly, even in Canada, the Black Loyalists faced discrimination. When the American Revolution ended, many people—blacks and whites—flooded into Nova Scotia. There was not enough food for all these newcomers to eat, or enough places to stay. The Black Loyalists were discriminated against and beaten up, just because of their skin colour.

As for the promise of a farm, some Black Loyalists waited six years before they received any land. Then they received only a tiny piece of land, much smaller than what they had been promised. The land was often rocky and far from the nearest town or water.

Many Black Loyalists found Canada bitterly cold. Some left and sailed to Africa. Others moved elsewhere in Canada in hopes of finding better conditions. But many of the Black Loyalists stayed in Nova Scotia and New Brunswick. Today, lots of families in the Maritimes can trace their ancestors back to these brave people.

"Black Loyalists"—Think About It!

1. What happened in 1775 in the United States?

_____

_____

2. Why did many black people become Black Loyalists during the American Revolution?

_____

_____

3. What did the British promise to Black Loyalists?

_____

_____

4. Why did many of the Black Loyalists leave Canada?

_____

_____

5. Did the Black Loyalists get what was promised to them by the government? Explain.

_____

_____

_____

6. Summarize the section titled "Heading to Canada."

_____

_____

_____

_____

_____

Gimli, Manitoba

Some towns and cities in Canada depended on immigrants to get their start. Gimli, Manitoba, is one of those towns.

New Iceland

Around 1875, natural disasters in Iceland left many people in the country with little to eat. Many Icelanders decided to leave their country, and a group of them chose to come to Canada.

About 200 of these immigrants arrived at a site on the west shore of Lake Winnipeg, north of Winnipeg, Manitoba. The Canadian government gave them land to live on and called the area New Iceland. The Icelanders named their settlement after the Hall of Gimli, which is known as *paradise* in Norse and Viking myths.

Life was tough for the New Icelanders. They experienced serious diseases, such as small pox, a highly contagious disease caused by a virus that results in a rash, extreme weakness, and a high fever. The settlers also faced extreme flooding.

Gimli Grows

Some of the New Icelanders left Gimli, but the ones who stayed developed schools, a newspaper, and a fishing industry on the lake. In just a few years, other nationalities were moving into the area, including people from Germany, Hungary, Poland, and Ukraine.

But Gimli has never forgotten its Icelandic roots. In 1967, a huge statue of a Viking was unveiled in Gimli. He is more than twice life size and stands proudly watching over the town.

The Gimli Glider

Gimli hit the news in 1983 when an airplane ran out of fuel on a flight between Montreal, Quebec, and Edmonton, Alberta. The plane was close to Gimli and the pilot knew there had once been an air force base there. The base had been closed for years, but the runway was still there. The pilot was certain he had to land the plane quickly or it would crash.

The pilot was also a glider pilot, so he was able to glide the plane to the Gimli air base. But when he got close, he discovered it was now a race car track and an event was taking place on the runway!

The pilot was able to avoid hitting anyone on the ground and land the plane safely. Not one of the plane's passengers was seriously hurt. The pilot's skill had prevented a horrible accident and Gimli became famous.

Gimli, Manitoba (continued)

Gimli Today

Each summer, Gimli celebrates its heritage during the Icelandic Festival of Manitoba, or Islendingadagurinn. More than 30,000 tourists flock to the event to sample traditional Icelandic dishes and see local artwork. The festival was first held in Winnipeg in 1890, and continued there until 1932, when it was moved to Gimli. It has been held in Gimli ever since. The Icelandic Festival of Manitoba is the second-oldest continuous ethnic festival in Canada.

Gimli also holds a film festival each summer. The movies are projected out onto a huge screen set up in the lake. The audience gathers on the shore of Lake Winnipeg to watch the show.

BRAIN STRETCH

Pretend you are the pilot who had to make the emergency landing at Gimli. Write a personal account of what happened. Make sure to include descriptive details of what was happening and how you felt.

_____

_____

_____

_____

_____

_____

_____

_____

_____

_____

"Gimli, Manitoba"—Think About It!

1. What forced many Icelandic people to leave their home country and come to Canada?

_____

_____

2. What is the Hall of Gimli? Why did the New Icelanders name their settlement after it?

_____

_____

_____

3. What other nationalities eventually moved into the area of Gimli?

_____

_____

4. Why do you think it is important for Canadians to celebrate ethnic cultures? Justify your thinking.

_____

_____

_____

_____

_____

_____

5. Summarize the events under the heading "The Gimli Glider."

_____

_____

_____

_____

6. The Icelandic Festival of Manitoba was not always held in Gimli. Explain.

_____

_____

Klondike Gold Rush

When gold was discovered in Canada's Yukon, there was a stampede north by would-be gold miners and people hoping to strike it rich. It was an incredible time in Canada's history.

Bonanza!

The area in Yukon where gold was found was known as the Klondike. It lies along the Klondike River, a name that evolved from the First Nations word *Tr'ondëk*, meaning "hammerstone water." Europeans found the word hard to say, and it eventually became Klondike.

Gold was discovered in August 1896 on a small river off the Klondike River. The stream was soon renamed Bonanza Creek—*bonanza* means "sudden great luck or wealth"—and it became world-famous. Tens of thousands of would-be miners left home and headed to the Klondike.

Chilkoot Pass

Most of the prospectors sailed up Canada's west coast from the United States. To get inland to the Klondike, the miners had to trek through the Coast Mountains of Alaska and northern British Columbia. The most famous part of the trek was the Chilkoot Pass.

This famous pass was a staircase 1,500 steps high and stretching far up into the surrounding mountains. Miners arrived there with all of their supplies and equipment. But the pass was too narrow for wagons or horses, so the miners had to carry everything on their backs, making many trips. In winter, the trail was covered with slippery ice. Workers cut out steps that became known as the "Golden Stairs." When a miners made it to the top of the slope, they dropped off their heavy load of equipment, then sat down and slid all the way back to the bottom to get the next load to carry up.

About 1,500 women trekked through the Chilkoot Pass. It was harder for them than for the men, since they had to wear long, heavy skirts, as well as petticoats and corsets. The women went along to cook for their husbands, fathers, and brothers, but for many women, there was another reason they made the long tough trip. The truth was that they did not want to miss out on the adventure! Some of the women also panned for gold, just as the men did.

A Lasting Legacy

Some miners became rich in the Klondike, while others found nothing. Another effect of the Gold Rush was that First Nations peoples were pushed aside and badly treated during gold fever. The Gold Rush also changed how people saw Canada's Far North. Around the world, people realized it is more than a barren wasteland and that there are many important activities and interesting people there. Gold is still mined in the area.

The influx of so many people changed Yukon. Dawson City was set up in 1896 and was the centre of the Gold Rush. It was the capital of Yukon until 1952, when Whitehorse was named the capital. That increased population also meant that the Northwest Territories were split up in 1898 and the new Yukon Territory (today, simply Yukon) was formed.

"Klondike Gold Rush"—Think About It!

1. List four facts about the Chilkoot Pass.

_____

_____

_____

2. List three ways the Gold Rush changed the Klondike.

_____

_____

_____

_____

3. When gold was discovered in Canada's Yukon, there was a stampede of people heading there. What is a *stampede*?

_____

_____

_____

4. Was climbing the Chilkoot Pass harder for women or for men? Why?

_____

_____

_____

5. Complete the table using information from the text and your ideas.

Cause	Effect
Klondike Gold Rush	

The **cause** is the reason something happens.

The **effect** is what happened.

Home Children

Poverty was everywhere on the streets of London, England, in the late 1800s. Especially affected were the many children who were orphaned and homeless. Some groups decided these children would have a chance for a better life in Canada. The children who were sent to the new country became known as "home children."

Sailing to Canada

These tiny immigrants were given the name "home children" because many of them had lived in orphanages, also known as *homes*. The migration was started by a number of women who felt sorry for the poverty-stricken children. They thought the clean air of Canada, and a chance to work and earn some money, would be wonderful for the children. The home children sailed to Canada in large groups. Most of them were between the ages of 8 and 16, with some as young as 4.

Difficult Times

When the children arrived in Canada, they were sent to various towns. They had no say about where they went. Many of the boys ended up on farms, where they worked in the field. One boy later said, "You would have thought that he was purchasing a horse, the way he sized up my forehead, body, and legs."

The girls were usually assigned household chores, on farms or in homes in towns. They were expected to do this work in exchange for a place to sleep, food, a small allowance, and the chance to go to school.

That would have been a real improvement over their old lives, but it was not the reality for many of the home children. Often they were treated like servants, and whipped and beaten. Some were starved.

Split Families

Also very difficult was that brothers and sisters were often separated, and sent to different farms or towns. "The brothers and sisters were all together," one home child said later. "And then they started grabbing the girls away from their brothers. I can still hear the screams of these kids being separated. Some of them never saw their sisters again."

The Home Children Grow Up

The home children program ended in the 1930s. More and more people became aware that the children were being unfairly treated. It was also revealed that the organizers back in Britain were making money by providing the children as cheap labour. Canadians felt these actions were wrong, as was taking the children from their home country. Many of the home children never returned to England. When they were old enough to leave the farms and homes where they had been placed, they got better-paying jobs, settled down, and made a new life in Canada.

"Home Children"—Think About It!

1. Who were the "home children"?

_____

_____

_____

2. Why did some people think life would be better for the home children in Canada?

_____

_____

_____

3. Do you agree or disagree with children being taken from their home country the way these children were? Explain.

_____

_____

_____

4. What do you think the boy who said, "You would have thought that he was purchasing a horse, the way he sized up my forehead, body, and legs" means?

_____

_____

_____

5. How were the home children treated when they arrived in Canada?

_____

_____

_____

6. What did the home children not have a choice about?

_____

_____

7. Why do you think many of the home children never returned to England?

_____

_____

_____

"Home Children"—Think About It! (continued)

8. What is your opinion? Do you think it was fair to the home children that other people were making money from the work they did?

   Make sure to include:

   - a topic sentence that states your opinion
   - two or three reasons that support your opinion
   - a concluding sentence that restates your opinion

Pier 21

From 1928 to 1971, many ships docked at Pier 21 in Halifax, Nova Scotia. It was the main harbour for immigrants arriving in Canada. More than one million settlers passed through Pier 21 as they began life in a new country.

"Gateway to Canada"

Pier 21 was just one of many terminals in Halifax harbour. But it became the landing place for ocean liners sailing across the Atlantic Ocean. In those days, most immigrants to Canada came from Britain, Italy, the Netherlands, Ukraine, and other European countries. They had to pass through inspection at Pier 21 before they were allowed to enter the country. So the facility became known as the "Gateway to Canada."

Arrival in Canada

When an immigrants left their ship at Pier 21, they walked along a gangplank to the dock. They proceeded to a reception area, where they were examined by a doctor. This exam was to make sure no immigrants had any serious diseases or health problems. If they did, they were quarantined and kept in a treatment area, or they were sent back to their home country.

Immigrants then met with immigration officials, who decided whether they could stay in the country. If the newcomers were allowed to remain in Canada, volunteers at Pier 21 helped them find food and a place to stay.

World War II

Pier 21 was very busy during World War II. The terminal was the departure point for 496,000 soldiers sailing across the Atlantic to fight the war in Europe. Even the members of the Royal Canadian Air Force sailed across the ocean—all available planes were needed to fight the enemy.

Later in the war, and after it was over, Pier 21 was busy welcoming *war brides*. These were women from many countries, but mostly from Britain, who met and married Canadian soldiers during the war. They came to Canada to live with their husbands. Many had children with them, who may never have seen their father before.

Pier 21 Today

Pier 21 closed its doors in 1971. By then, most immigrants came to Canada by plane, entering the country through its international airports. Very few newcomers arrived through Pier 21.

In 1999, Pier 21 reopened its doors, this time as the Canadian Museum of Immigration at Pier 21. There, you can find out about the many brave immigrants who arrived at Pier 21. You can hear their stories and see movies about their experiences.

Today, approximately one in every five Canadians has a direct link to Pier 21, all thanks to their immigrant ancestors who came to Canada seeking a better life.

"Pier 21"—Think About It!

1. How did Pier 21 become known as the "Gateway to Canada"?

   _____

   _____

   _____

   _____

2. During World War II, Pier 21 was very busy. Circle True or False.   True   False
   If false, write the correct statement.

   _____

3. What does the term *war brides* mean?

   _____

   _____

   _____

4. What happened to Pier 21 in 1971? Why did this happen?

   _____

   _____

   _____

   _____

5. What happened to Pier 21 in 1999? What can you do there now?

   _____

   _____

   _____

   _____

6. Explain the steps that immigrants were required to follow when they first left their ships at Pier 21.

   _____

   _____

   _____

   _____

Why Immigrants Choose Canada

Canada has a cold climate that can make life difficult. Despite this, there are many reasons why people choose to move to and settle in Canada.

Safe and Secure

Some people who move to Canada have survived wars in their country and want a safer place to live. Those people, often called *refugees*, may have lost family members or had their homes destroyed. Other immigrants flee because they are in danger because of their political beliefs. In some countries, citizens are put in jail if they do not agree with the nation's leaders. In Canada, people are allowed to disagree with the government and state their views.

After surviving wars and dangers, immigrants appreciate Canada's stability. They are grateful that Canada is a peaceful country, where people help each other. Immigrants also come to Canada because the country has a good health care system. Not only is it effective and modern, but it also provides care for every Canadian.

A Better Tomorrow

There are many immigrants who choose to live in Canada because they believe there are more opportunities here for them and for their children. For example, some countries do not respect girls' and women's rights the way Canada does.

People also come to Canada because of the excellent schools for themselves and their children. They know that education is a great way to land a good job. In some countries, girls are not allowed to go to school. Parents who want their daughters to learn and grow appreciate the opportunities that Canada can offer them.

Canada has many business possibilities for immigrants and for people born in Canada. The country is rich in natural resources, such as oil, gas, timber, and minerals. Canada also has advanced technology and computer companies that need employees and can offer well-paying jobs.

A Good Place to Live

Some people who move to Canada are looking for an adventure and a new life in a new country. Canada is the second-largest country in the world, with lots of beautiful rugged scenery, opportunities to take part in exciting sports, and many other attractions.

Because Canada is so large, it offers immigrants a variety of places to live. People who want to live by the ocean can choose Canada's east coast or west coast. Those who like to live in the mountains have lots of places from which to choose. Canada's prairies offer wide-open spaces, while big-city living appeals to others.

Canada encourages people to share their cultures and traditions. Immigrants appreciate our country's multiculturalism, which allows them both to keep ties to their home country and to enjoy all that Canada can offer.

Create a collage! Look through Canadian newspapers, magazines, community flyers, and advertisements. Cut out examples of how people share their culture and traditions, and paste them in the space below.

"Why Immigrants Choose Canada"—Think About It! (continued)

1. Complete the concept map using information from the text.

A **main idea** is what the text is mostly about.
A **subheading** is the title given to a part of a text.
A **detail** is important information that tells more about the main idea.

Concept Map

Main Idea

Subheading

Subheading

Subheading

Details

Details

Details

"Why Immigrants Choose Canada"—Think About It! (continued)

2. What is your opinion? Do you think it is fair that in some countries you cannot go to school if you are a girl?

   Make sure to include:

   - a topic sentence that states your opinion
   - two or three reasons that support your opinion
   - a concluding sentence that restates your opinion

3. Create a brochure to persuade immigrants to choose Canada as their new home.

Brochure Outline

A *brochure* is a booklet or pamphlet that contains descriptive information. Choose a topic for your brochure. Topics may include something that you are studying in school or something that interests you.

STEP 1: Plan Your Brochure

STEP	COMPLETION
1. Take a piece of paper and fold the paper the same way your brochure will be folded.	
2. Before writing the brochure, plan the layout in pencil. Write the heading for each section where you would like it to be in the brochure. Leave room underneath each section to write information. Also leave room for graphics or drawings.	

STEP 2: Complete a Draft

STEP	COMPLETION
1. Research information for each section of your brochure.	
2. Read your draft for meaning, then add, delete, or change words to improve your writing.	

STEP 3: Final Editing Checklist

☐ I checked the spelling.　　　　☐ My brochure is neat and organized.

☐ I checked the punctuation.　　　☐ My brochure has drawings or graphics.

☐ I checked for clear sentences.　☐ My brochure is attractive.

In Flanders Fields

Every November 11, people in many countries buy poppies to show they remember brave soldiers and are proud of them. Do you know why the poppy is the symbol of Remembrance Day? It is because of a Canadian doctor who wrote the most famous war poem ever, "In Flanders Fields."

John McCrae

A Brave Doctor

By the time World War I began in Europe in 1914, John McCrae had been a doctor for many years and had already served in the South African (Boer) War. McCrae was born in Guelph, Ontario, in 1872 and had been writing poetry all his life.

By April 1915, McCrae was in an area of Belgium known as Flanders. The courageous doctor was in charge of a medical centre in the middle of the battle raging there. He tried to treat the injured men, but dead and wounded soldiers kept rolling down into his dugout operating station. McCrae barely had time to eat and sleep—there was not even time for him to change his clothes.

Death of a Friend

In early May, a good friend of McCrae's was shot and killed in battle. McCrae sadly buried his friend, but wanted to do something more. He could no longer help his friend or any of the other dead soldiers around him. But McCrae knew that if he wrote a poem about them, he could tell of their lives and perhaps it would help people remember them.

Looking around, McCrae saw the blood-red poppies blowing in the wind in a nearby cemetery. They inspired him to write "In Flanders Fields." But he did not think the poem was very good and threw it away!

Luckily, another officer found the poem and realized how great it was. He sent it to magazines and newspapers in England and it was published in December 1915. The poem was an immediate success and it inspired people around the world.

McCrae continued to care for wounded soldiers in Belgium and France. He worked very hard. But, in January 1918, he came down with pneumonia. By the end of the month, this quiet but famous soldier, doctor, and poet was dead.

In Flanders Fields (continued)

Still Remembered

McCrae's poem raised soldiers' and civilians' spirits during World War I. Organizers in Canada hoped the poem would help raise $150 million to support soldiers and others, but it brought in almost three times that amount.

Every year, Remembrance Day is celebrated on November 11 at 11 a.m., because that is the date and time in 1918 when the agreement that finally ended World War I was signed. Poppies are mentioned in McCrae's famous poem and that is one of the main reasons the flower was chosen as a symbol of remembrance.

IN FLANDERS FIELDS

In Flanders fields the poppies blow
Between the crosses, row on row,
That mark our place; and in the sky
The larks, still bravely singing, fly
Scarce heard amid the guns below.

We are the Dead. Short days ago,
We lived, felt dawn, saw sunset glow,
Loved, and were loved, and now we lie
In Flanders fields.

Take up our quarrel with the foe:
To you from failing hands we throw
The torch; be yours to hold it high.
If ye break faith with us who die
We shall not sleep, though poppies grow
In Flanders fields.

"In Flanders Fields"—Think About It!

1. Why do you think "In Flanders Fields" was such a successful poem?

_____

_____

_____

2. What is your favourite line in the poem? Explain what you like about this line.

_____

_____

_____

3. What was John McCrae's role when he was stationed in Flanders during World War I?

_____

_____

_____

4. John McCrae was very brave. What were some of the ways he showed his courage?

_____

_____

_____

5. What do you think these lines from the poem mean:
   To you from failing hands we throw
   The torch; be yours to hold it high.

_____

_____

6. What do you think the word *lark* means? Use the poem to help determine the meaning.

_____

_____

_____

Camp X

Just east of Toronto, Ontario, is a small town that had a big secret during World War II. Whitby, located on the shores of Lake Ontario, was home to Camp X, a training school for spies from Canada, Britain, and other countries fighting on the side of the Allied forces during the war.

While the conflict raged in Europe, the camp was top-secret, since enemy spies would have loved to destroy it. But after World War II ended in 1945, people around the world discovered the incredible story of Camp X.

"Intrepid"

The founder of Camp X was a businessman, inventor, and spy named William Stephenson. First, he set up a spy network in New York. The network's telegraph address was "Intrepid" (which means "bold and courageous"), and that became Stephenson's code name.

Intrepid then set up Camp X on the site of an old farm. Hundreds of men and women trained at the camp, including Ian Fleming, who wrote the series of books about James Bond. Some people claim Fleming based Bond on Stephenson! Intrepid was one of the most famous spies of World War II. People say Intrepid was one of the most important people fighting for the Allies in World War II. He accomplished so much—yet had only a Grade 6 education.

Parachutes, Sabotage, and Disguises

At Camp X, spies were taught how to decipher (or break) enemy codes, forge (create fake) documents (it could cause confusion for the enemy), as well as how to sabotage experiments the German were conducting on atomic power. They learned how to shoot guns and explode bombs, kill enemies silently, and jump from a parachute. Radio operators were also trained here.

Spies had to be very fit, so they were constantly exercising and training. They also learned to survive with little food, to read maps, create disguises, write secret messages, and do all the other things they would need to do in their dangerous work.

At Camp X, Stephenson also helped maintain a complex telecommunications centre called Hydra. It was located at Camp X because it was safe to code and decode messages there, far from the listening ears of enemy radio operators.

Camp X Today

Today, you can visit a park where Camp X stood. You will see the craters where spies were trained to use explosives. You can also see the pathway the guards used as they patrolled the camp and kept its secrets safe from prying eyes. You can also visit a monument dedicated to the brave men and women who trained and worked there.

Nearby is a museum about the spy school. There, you will see forged money from various European countries, a comb with a hidden compass, a suitcase radio, and much more.

"Camp X"—Think About It!

1. Why was it so important that Camp X remain a secret during the war? Use evidence from the text to support your answer.

_____

_____

_____

2. Why do you think the author mentioned that William Stephenson had only a Grade 6 education?

_____

_____

3. Look at the subheading Parachutes, Sabotage, and Disguises. How does this subheading make you feel about being a spy? If this subheading were placed on a poster advertising a spy job, would it persuade you to try to become a spy?

_____

_____

_____

4. List some words that can be used to describe spies.

_____

_____

_____

5. William "Intrepid" Stephenson maintained Hydra, a sophisticated telecommunications centre. Why else do you think some people think he was so important?

_____

_____

_____

6. How is Camp X today different from how it was during World War II?

_____

_____

Fathers of Confederation

In 1867, Canada became a country. This confederation, or union, of a number of separate colonies was due to the hard work of a group of men who became known as the Fathers of Confederation.

Canada in Danger

By the 1860s, it was clear to the colonies in what is now Canada that it was time to make a change. The United States was a large and prosperous country, and was threatening to take over the group of colonies. In the past, Great Britain had defended its Canadian colonies, but Britain no long wanted to pay for this defence.

There were more difficulties within the colonies. The colonies were not growing quickly because the lack of transportation between colonies made it difficult for them to sell goods to one another.

On July 1, 1867, New Brunswick, Nova Scotia, Ontario (formerly Upper Canada), and Québec (formerly Lower Canada) joined together to become stronger and more successful. The Fathers of Confederation dreamed of a powerful new nation stretching from the Atlantic Ocean to the Pacific Ocean.

The Most Famous Fathers of Confederation

There were 36 Fathers of Confederation. Probably the best known was John A. Macdonald. "Whatever you do, adhere to the Union," said Macdonald. "We are a great country, and shall become one of the greatest in the universe if we preserve it …" Macdonald worked so hard to make confederation happen that he was elected as the first prime minister of Canada.

Another Father of Confederation, Charles Tupper, also became one of Canada's prime ministers. But he was in office for only 69 days, in 1896, making him the shortest-serving prime minister ever. Thomas D'Arcy McGee was another Father of Confederation. He was known as the best public speaker of his time.

The Country Grows

Thanks to the Fathers of Confederation and their work, the country continued to grow. The rest of the provinces and territories joined Confederation in the following years:

1870: Manitoba, Northwest Territories

1871: British Columbia

1873: Prince Edward Island

1898: Yukon

1905: Alberta, Saskatchewan

1949: Newfoundland and Labrador

1999: Nunavut

Fathers of Confederation (continued)

Modern Fathers of Confederation

You might say Joey Smallwood and Paul Okalik are 20th-century Fathers of Confederation. Smallwood campaigned hard to have Newfoundland and Labrador join the country. After a close vote, Newfoundland and Labrador became a province of Canada in 1949, with Smallwood as its first premier. When Nunavut became a territory in 1999, Okalik was chosen as the first premier of Nunavut by the territory's first Legislative Assembly.

Think About It!

1. Do you think it was a good idea for Canada's provinces to unite? Justify your thinking.

_____

_____

_____

2. What is a *confederation*?

_____

_____

3. Why can Joey Smallwood and Paul Okalik be considered Fathers of Confederation?

_____

_____

_____

_____

4. How many provinces first joined Canada? Which provinces were they?

_____

_____

_____

5. List three reasons the provinces united to form one country.

_____

_____

_____

_____

Biography of a Famous Canadian

Complete a timeline of the significant events in the life a famous Canadian. Use the graphic organizer to help you.

Name of person: _____

I chose this famous Canadian because...

_____

_____

_____

_____

_____

Pretend you are a reporter. What questions would you ask this person?

_____

_____

_____

_____

_____

_____

_____

_____

_____

Biography of a Famous Canadian (continued)

Use this graphic organizer to record significant events in the life of the famous Canadian you have chosen.

Date	Event

Biography of a Famous Canadian (continued)

Use this graphic organizer to record significant events in the life of the famous Canadian you have chosen.

Date	Event

Sir John A. Macdonald

Canada's first prime minister, Sir John A. Macdonald, had worked hard to bring the country together. He dreamed of a nation stretching from the Atlantic Ocean to the Pacific Ocean—and he made his dream come true.

From Scotland to Canada

Macdonald was born in Glasgow, Scotland, in 1815. When he was just five years old, his family moved to Upper Canada, known today as Ontario. Macdonald became a lawyer when he grew up. People liked him because he had a good sense of humour and a remarkable ability to remember their names.

Life in Politics

In 1843, Macdonald entered politics. By the 1860s, the colonies (now provinces) in what is today Canada knew it was time for change. The United States was threatening to take them over. As well, the colonies were not growing and developing. One reason was because transportation between the colonies was not very good.

The colonies began to think about banding together to become more successful and stronger. Macdonald thought this was a very good idea. He worked hard to make people see how important it was for the colonies to become one country. Macdonald and the other 35 men involved in the union became known as the Fathers of Confederation.

Confederation

On July 1, 1867, the new country of Canada was formed. It consisted of only the provinces of New Brunswick, Nova Scotia, Ontario, and Quebec (formerly Lower Canada). But Macdonald was convinced it could grow and prosper. Because he had worked so hard to bring about Confederation, Macdonald was named the new country's first prime minister.

As time went by, more of the colonies joined Canada and the country kept growing. For example, British Columbia joined in 1871, after Macdonald promised to build a railway to the Pacific to link the country.

In 1885, the railway was completed. The next year, Macdonald and his wife, Lady Agnes, rode the train to the Pacific. When they rode through Kicking Horse Pass in British Columbia, the couple sat out on the front of the train! Macdonald was 71 years old at the time.

Parks and Mounties

Macdonald brought many other changes to Canada. In 1873, he set up the North-West Mounted Police, which would later become the Royal Canadian Mounted Police. In 1885, he also set up the country's first national park in Banff, Alberta.

Macdonald died in 1891. He was prime minister of Canada for 19 years. Only one other prime minister, William Lyon Mackenzie King, has been prime minister longer.

"Sir John A. Macdonald"—Think About It!

Complete the concept web using information from the text.

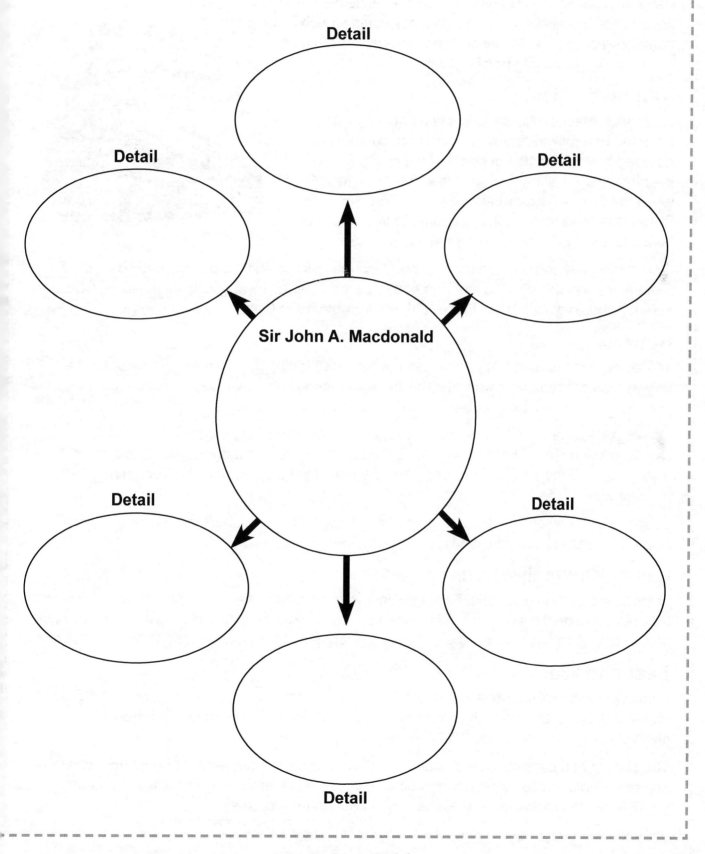

Detail

Detail

Detail

Sir John A. Macdonald

Detail

Detail

Detail

Canadian Pacific Railway

Canada became a new country in 1867. To unite such a huge nation, a railway had to be built that would stretch from the east coast to the west coast. The railway became known as the Canadian Pacific Railway.

Ribbon of Steel

Sir John A. Macdonald, Canada's first prime minister, dreamed of a railway that would cross the country.. He believed that this "ribbon of steel" would help hold the country together. He would see his vision realized in 1886, when the first passenger train rolled into Port Moody, British Columbia, on July 4. But getting to this point would take a lot of work and involve thousands of workers.

First, the survey crews headed out. It was their job to try to find the flattest and most direct route for the railway. But the line also had to be safe and as inexpensive as possible, which meant it should avoid places that would require workers to build tunnels or bridges.

Navvies

The surveying began in 1871 and was not completed until 1881. By then, the route for the railway was chosen and it was time to start laying the track. Crews began work at both the west end and the east end at the same time, to lay down the track as quickly as possible.

The workers were called "navvies"—they got their name from the men who had built water channels known as navigation canals. These railway workers cut down trees and cleared a wide path, called the *roadbed*, along the line the surveyors had marked. Then they used ploughs to level the ground for the tracks.

Despite the surveyors' best efforts, sometimes bridges had to be built for the railway. They spanned rivers and canyons and required a lot hard, dangerous work.

Laying Down the Track

Track-laying crews came next. First, they laid wooden railway ties across the roadbed. Then, they placed a steel rail on each side of the ties. Iron spikes held the rails in place. The workers spread gravel and soil around the ties to keep them steady, then moved on to the next section.

East and West

Workers in the east had to blast through the Canadian Shield, which is some of the hardest rock in the world. Long pieces of track also sank and were lost in patches of muskeg, or, marsh.

The section of the railway that was built in British Columbia often wound through mountains and over rivers. It was extremely difficult to work around. Crews used dynamite to tunnel through rock and it was dangerous work that killed many workers.

"Canadian Pacific Railway"—Think About It!

1. What was the purpose of the Canadian Pacific Railway?

_____

_____

2. What is a *navvie*?

_____

_____

3. What kinds of work did navvies do?

_____

_____

_____

4. Why did the government want to avoid building bridges and tunnels while building the railway?

_____

_____

5. How was the work that was required to build the Canadian Pacific Railway dangerous?

_____

_____

_____

6. What was the date when the first passenger train arrived at Port Moody station in British Columbia?

_____

_____

7. Summarize the steps taken to build the Canadian Pacific Railway.

_____

_____

_____

_____

The Famous Five

It is hard to believe that about 100 years ago, women could not vote and had few of the rights that men enjoyed. That situation changed thanks to the hard work of many brave women, including a group that became known as the Famous Five.

The Fight for Rights

Nellie McClung, Louise McKinney, Henrietta Muir Edwards, Emily Murphy, and Irene Parlby were the women who made up the Famous Five. They were well-educated women who worked in Alberta to improve the lives of women there and across the country. These strong, determined women felt it was important that everyone be treated fairly and equally. So they fought for a minimum wage for women, and battled to increase the rights of farm women.

Nellie McClung was already well known because she had fought for women in western Canada to gain the right to vote in provincial elections. "Never retract, never explain, never apologize— get things done and let them howl," McClung once said.

Women Are Not Persons

The Famous Five were brought together by member Emily Murphy. Murphy had been hired as a magistrate, which is a kind of judge. But, on her first day of work in 1916, a lawyer told her she had no right to be there. The lawyer claimed that, according to the British North America (BNA) Act, a woman was not a person, and only a person could be a magistrate.

This same problem came up when women's groups were pushing the Canadian government to make Murphy the country's first female senator. People argued that a woman could not be appointed to the Senate because she was not a person.

The Famous Five Forms

Being told she was not a person annoyed and frustrated Murphy. She discovered that she needed a group of five to challenge the ruling. So, in 1927, the Famous Five was formed to send a petition to the Supreme Court of Canada—the top law court in the country—to find out if the word "person" in the BNA Act included women. After debating for five weeks, the court decided against the Famous Five.

The Persons Case

The women were shocked. But, as Murphy once said, "Whenever I don't know whether to fight or not, I fight!" They took their case, which was now known as the Persons Case, to the Privy Council of England. At the time, it was Canada's absolute highest court.

On October 18, 1929, the Council declared women were legally persons and could hold any appointed or elected office. Finally, the Famous Five had won! Their hard work still inspires women today.

"The Famous Five"—Think About It!

1. Read the text again, then suggest two other possible attention-grabbing titles for it.

   _____

   _____

   _____

2. List five facts about the Famous Five.

   _____

   _____

   _____

   _____

   _____

3. Why was Emily Murphy told she could not be a magistrate?

   _____

   _____

   _____

4. Why do you think Nellie McClung felt it was important for women to vote?

   _____

   _____

   _____

   _____

   _____

5. The Famous Five sent a petition to the Supreme Court of Canada. What does *supreme* mean?

   _____

6. In what way do you think life would be different for women today if they could not vote?

   _____

   _____

   _____

Old Money, New Money

It is hard to imagine there was once a time when money did not exist. But thousands of years ago, people traded, or bartered, with each other to get what they needed. For instance, if someone needed a cow, she might trade a few chickens for it.

But trading takes time, and it is difficult to move cows and chickens around for bartering. So people began using coins and pieces of paper to represent animals, food, and other items.

Salt, Feathers, and Whales' Teeth

Metal coins have been used in various countries for money for about 3,000 years. People started using paper money about 1,000 years ago, because it was lighter to carry than coins.

Blankets, feathers, tea leaves, and even whales' teeth have also been used for money. Long ago in ancient Rome, workers were paid not with coins but with salt. That is where the word salary comes from—sal means salt in Latin, the Romans' language.. In Canada in the late 1600s, there was a shortage of coins, so playing cards were used instead. The amount of money was written on the back of the card.

Some First Nations in North America used shell beads known as wampum for trade, in ceremonies for decoration, and to record agreements. It is hard to believe, but huge stone doughnuts were used as money by the people of Yap, which is an island in the Pacific Ocean. Some of the stones were so large they would not even fit in your bedroom!

Coins and Bills

People used to use 25¢ bills in Canada and the United States. These and other bills that were worth less than $1 were known across North America as shinplasters because they looked similar to a small, square piece of paper that was used at the time as a bandage.

Coins last longer than bills because metal is strong and durable. Money that lasts longer is less expensive to produce since it does not have to be replaced as frequently. That is good for the environment too. So many countries have switched from bills to coins for some of their money. Did you know that Canada used to have $1 and $2 bills? The government has even talked about changing the $5 bill to a coin!

Modern Money

Paper money may last as little as two years. That is why countries such as Canada and others are now printing polymer bills—sometimes called "plastic money." These bills are stronger than paper and cleaner too, since they do not absorb liquid.

Countries are always looking for ways to make their bills difficult to counterfeit, or copy. Some bills have transparent sections, raised type, metallic images, holograms, and more. Other bills include Braille dots so visually impaired people can use them more easily.

"Old Money, New Money"—Think About It!

1. Have you ever traded to get something? What did you trade?

_____

_____

_____

2. Why do you think people stopped using large stone doughnuts as money?

_____

_____

_____

3. If you are a "penny-pincher," you are good at saving money. What do you think the expression "put your money where your mouth is" means?

_____

_____

_____

4. Use evidence from the text to describe the advantages of using coins instead of paper money.

_____

_____

_____

5. What changes do you think could be made to the coins or bills you use every day to make them more difficult to counterfeit and longer-lasting?

_____

_____

_____

6. Money tells people about a country and the people who live there. On a separate piece of paper, design a $10 bill that represents you and your community.

Canada's Imports and Exports

Canada is a country that depends on *trade*. Trade is the importing and exporting of goods to and from other countries.

Countries trade with each other when they do not have the resources, or the ability to meet their own needs and wants on their own.

Imports are goods that a country purchases from or trades for with other countries. Countries import items from other countries around the world for several reasons. They may not be able to produce or grow the item, such as oranges. Or, another country might be specialists at producing a specific product that they want. Sometimes it may actually be easier and cheaper to buy a product from another country than it is to make it at home. Some of Canada's major imports include cars, car parts, fruits, vegetables, and technology.

Exports are goods that are for sale or exchange from Canada to other countries. Some of Canada's major exports include aluminum, precious metals, metal ores, newsprint, lumber, wood pulp, wheat, natural gas, petroleum, and technology.

Think About It!

1. What is *trade*?

   _____

2. What are *exports*?

   _____

3. List Canada's major exports mentioned in the text.

   _____

   _____

   _____

4. What are *imports*?

   _____

   _____

5. List Canada's major imports mentioned in the text.

   _____

   _____

"Canada's Imports and Exports"—Think About It! (continued)

6. Complete the chart below by researching the following:

- five products from around your home or school, such as clothing or food items, that are imported from other countries
- five products that are exported from Canada to other countries

Canada's Imports

Product	Country of Origin

Canada's Exports

Product	Country Exported to

What surprised you in your findings? Explain your thinking.

___

___

___

___

Cool Canadian Inventions

Canada is a country of amazing inventors. Here are just a few of the many incredible devices, sports, tools, and more that have been invented here!

Getting Around

Thousands of years ago, Aboriginal peoples invented canoes, toboggans, and snowshoes. Inuit inventors even created sunglasses to make it easier to see when snow reflects bright sunshine. In 1922, Joseph-Armand Bombardier of Quebec invented the snowmobile to make it easier to get around in winter in Canada's north.

In 1930, John D. Millar of Ontario had the idea of painting lines on the road to make driving safer. By 1933, this invention had spread across North America.

Some Canadian inventions have headed into space. The anti-gravity suit keeps astronauts—and pilots—safe while flying. The Canadarm, first used in 1981, repairs and positions satellites for the astronauts on the International Space Station.

Having Fun

Canadians like to have fun. Did you know that the Jolly Jumper for babies, the tabletop hockey game, and IMAX films were all invented in Canada?

Canadian James Naismith invented basketball in 1891, the first five-pin bowling game was played in Toronto in 1908, and Canadian swimmer Peg Seller created synchronized swimming in 1924.

Getting Things Done

Canadian inventor Peter L. Robertson was tired of screwdrivers that slipped out of the screws. So he invented a square-headed screwdriver and screws with a square socket on them. Workers around the world loved it, and his invention became known as the Robertson screwdriver.

Norman Breakey of Toronto invented the paint roller in 1940 to speed up painting jobs. Cleanup became easier in the 1950s when Canadians Harry Wasylyk and Larry Hanson invented the green garbage bag.

In 1937, scientists at the University of Toronto built the first electron microscope. It allowed people to see viruses and other tiny things that had been invisible to the human eye until then.

To keep people healthy, John Hopps of Toronto invented the pacemaker in 1950. This device sends pulses of electricity to a person's heart to make it beat regularly. Dr. Tofy Mussivand of Ottawa created the world's first artificial human heart in the 1990s for people with damaged hearts.

© Chalkboard Publishing

"Cool Canadian Inventions"—Think About It!

1. What items did Canada's Aboriginal peoples invent?

   _____

   _____

2. How did Joseph-Armand Bombardier make it easier to getting around in winter?

   _____

   _____

3. Which Canadian inventions travelled into space?

   _____

4. List the inventions Canadians made to have fun.

   _____

   _____

   _____

5. Describe the special screwdriver invented by Peter L. Robertson.

   _____

   _____

   _____

6. How might the invention of the electron microscope benefit doctors and people who are sick? Use the text and your own ideas to explain.

   _____

   _____

   _____

7. What did John Hopps invent and what does it do?

   _____

   _____

8. What do you think an artificial heart might do? Explain.

   _____

   _____

   _____

Living Things

You know that our world is made up of living and non-living things. A bird is a living thing. A rock is not. But what makes something alive? We are alive, but so is a tree. What do we have in common with a tree?

Characteristics of Living Things

Living things are called organisms. All organisms share certain characteristics:

- **Organisms are made up of one or more cells.** Cells are the basic unit of life. They are the smallest unit of living matter. Some organisms, such as bacteria, have just one cell. They are unicellular. Other organisms, such as humans, have many cells. They are multicellular.

- **Organisms use materials and energy from their environment to grow and develop.** Humans eat food. With the help of water, their bodies turn the food into energy. Green plants use sunlight and water to make their own food for energy.

- **Organisms respond to their environment.** A cat might respond to a loud sound by running away. Flowers respond to sunlight by turning toward the Sun.

- **Organisms respire.** This means they exchange gases with their environment. Animals and humans breathe in air (oxygen) and breathe out carbon dioxide. Plants do the opposite when they are making food. They take in carbon dioxide and release oxygen.

- **Organisms reproduce.** They can produce copies of themselves. Bacteria reproduce by splitting in two. Some plants reproduce through seeds. Some animals lay eggs. Other animals give birth to live young.

Needs of Living Things

To stay alive, organisms must meet their needs. These needs include food and water to get the energy they need to grow, develop, and reproduce. They need air to get the gases they need. They need the right place to live (habitat), which will provide everything they need to stay alive.

"Living Things"—Think About It!

1. Choose an organism that you know a lot about. You might choose an animal such as a rabbit, or a plant such as a potato plant. On a separate piece of paper, write a paragraph explaining how you know your choice is a living thing.

2. Look at the chart below.

   a) Write what each item is made of.   b) Circle the items that are living.

Item	Made out of
gold ring	
cheese	
paper	
wool scarf	
glass jar	

3. Choose an animal that lives in your environment. Explain how the animal meets its needs for food and water.

_____

_____

_____

_____

_____

4. Temperature is important to living things. Some organisms can survive where the temperature is very hot. Some can survive where the temperature is very cold. Temperature is part of which need? Why?

_____

_____

_____

_____

_____

Classifying Organisms

There are many types of life on Earth. All living things share certain characteristics, so they all belong to one group: organisms. Scientists believe there are over 10 million types of organisms on Earth. Classifying organisms helps scientists study them and understand them better.

Characteristics are used to classify an organism. Characteristics include what the parts of the organism do. What the organism looks like inside and outside is another characteristic.

The most common classification system divides organisms into five kingdoms: Plantae, Animalia, Fungi, Monera, Protista. Within each kingdom, organisms are divided into smaller groups. Within those groups, they are divided into even smaller groups. As the groups are divided further, the organisms become more alike. As you see in the chart below, there are more similarities in plants in the same family than in plants in the same phylum.

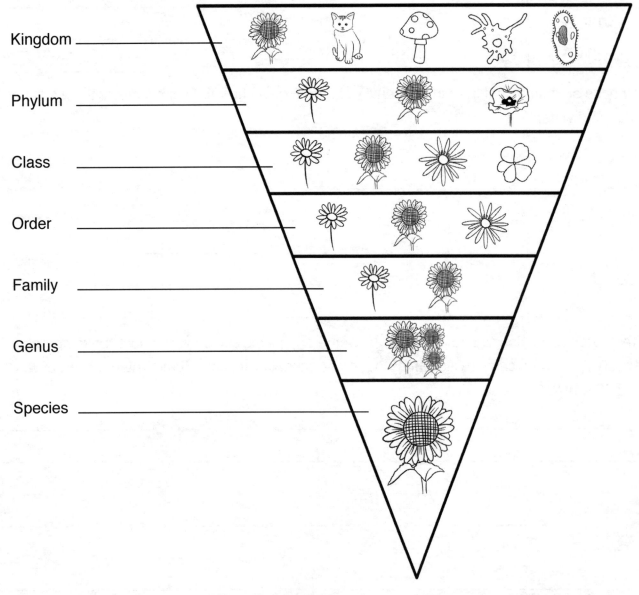

Kingdom

Phylum

Class

Order

Family

Genus

Species

1. Name the five kingdoms the most comman classification system uses.

_____

_____

2. Why is it important for all scientists to use the same classification system?

_____

_____

3. You have six animals to classify in the flow chart below: sea star, squirrel, lion, trout, whale, and sparrow. Use common characteristics to categorize the first group into two groups. Then divide each group into two groups. Keep dividing groups until you have only one animal in a category. (You may not need to use all the boxes.) In each box, write the characteristic you are using to classify the animals, then the name of the animals. For example, one classification may be "Has fur: lion, squirrel" and "Does not have fur: sparrow."

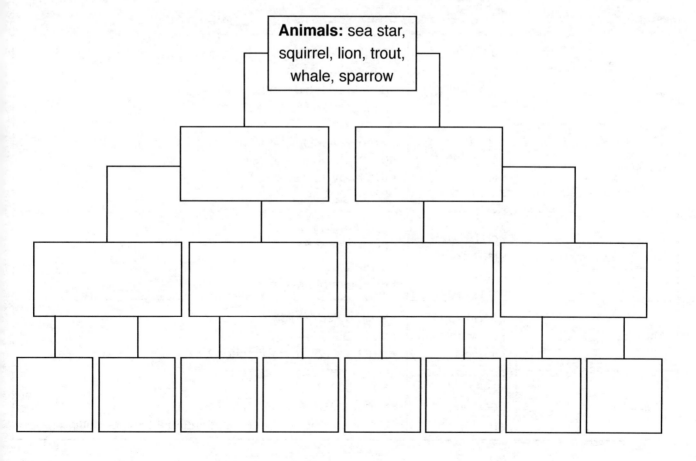

The Animal Kingdom

All animals share these characteristics:

- multicellular
- rely on other organisms for food
- can move around or move parts of their bodies to get food
- most need two individuals to reproduce

All animals can be divided into two main groups: vertebrates and invertebrates. Vertebrates have a spinal cord surrounded by a backbone. Invertebrates do not. All vertebrates are in the phylum Chordata, which includes amphibians, reptiles, birds, fish, and mammals. Invertebrates are divided into many phyla (the plural of phylum). These include annelids (worms), and mollusks such as snails and clams. The phylum Arthropod has sub-phyla that contain insects, crustaceans, and arachnids.

Only about 5% of animals are vertebrates. How much do you know about invertebrates?

Characteristics of Invertebrates

Phylum/Sub-phylum	Examples	Characteristics
Insects	• butterfly • ant • grasshopper • fly	• six jointed legs • three body parts • almost all have wings • exoskeleton (outer skeleton)
Arachnids	• spider • scorpion • tick • mite	• usually eight jointed legs • exoskeleton • two body sections • lay eggs
Crustaceans	• crab • lobster • barnacle	• exoskeleton • two body parts • jointed legs or claws • two pairs of antennae
Annelids	• earthworm • flatworm • leech	• segmented bodies • no limbs • most are covered with short bristles
Mollusks	• snail • octopus • oyster	• soft body • either external or internal shell • a foot used for moving, attaching to things, or getting food

"The Animal Kingdom"—Think About It!

1. Explain why a bullfrog is an animal.

_____

_____

2. Why do you think humans are more familiar with vertebrates than with other animals?

_____

_____

_____

3. Why are insects, arachnids, and crustaceans in the same phylum?

_____

_____

4. What do insects have that makes them different from other invertebrates?

_____

_____

5. Complete the web below by adding the characteristics of each class of vertebrates. Use what you know, and check references if necessary. Try to add at least three for each. Share your web with a classmate. Do you agree with each other's characteristics?

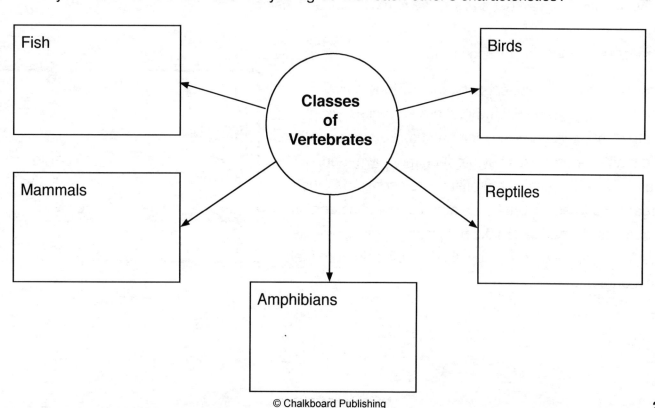

The Forgotten Kingdoms

People rarely think about organisms in the Monera, Protista, and Fungi kingdoms.

The Monera Kingdom

- have only one cell
- have simplest cell structure
- reproduce by splitting in two
- most absorb nutrients from outside their bodies

Bacteria are everywhere. They turn milk into yogurt and cheese. They help decompose waste. They can keep us healthy or make us sick. They are used to produce many medicines that treat diseases. Although we cannot see them, bacteria are very important in our lives.

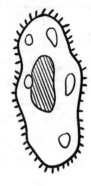

bacteria

The Protista Kingdom

- do not fit in any other kingdom
- are not bacteria, fungi, plants, or animals
- most have only one cell
- have more complex cell structure than monerans
- live mostly in water, but can survive in moist soil and inside animals
- most reproduce by splitting in two

Protists are classified according to how they move and how they get nutrition. So, there are animal-like protists, plant-like protists, and fungus-like protists. Algae are plant-like protists. They produce their own food. Amoebas are animal-like protists. They consume other organisms for food. Drinking water that contains certain types of amoebas can make people sick. Slime moulds are fungus-like protists. They absorb nutrients from their environment.

algae

The Fungi Kingdom

- have many cells
- get nutrients from dead plants and animals
- are decomposers that help turn dead organisms into nutrients that make soil rich

Fungi are used to produce many medicines. We eat some types of fungi. Yeast is a fungus used for baking. Some fungi can cause infections, such as athlete's foot and ringworm. Others can damage crops.

mushroom

Think About It!

1. Summarize what you have learned about the Monera, Protista, and Fungi kingdoms. Decide on the categories of information. Write those as column headings. For example, you could use "Cells" and "Getting Nutrition" as headings. You can research these kingdoms to find the information you need.

Monera					
Protista					
Fungi					

Biodiversity

Scientists estimate that there are 1.7 million species of animals and plants in the world. This means that there is amazing diversity of life on our planet. Most species tend to live in specific areas, or habitats. In these habitats, they can find the things they need to stay alive.

Classifications of Habitats

Scientists classify habitats the same way they classify organisms: by their characteristics. Scientists have not agreed on one system of classification for habitats. But all systems used are based on similar plant, animal, and climatic features. The systems start with large groups that are further divided into smaller and smaller groups.

The largest groups of habitats are biomes. There are many types of biomes. Examples include deserts, forests, grasslands, tundra, and oceans. Each of these groups is divided into smaller groups. For example, the forest groups include boreal, subarctic, subtropical, and temperate.

Scientists study organisms in smaller areas to better understand them. They study how the organisms interact with each other and with the environment. The environment includes non-living things such as soil, water, air, heat, and light. A habitat community is made up of the set of organisms that live within a certain area. The area could be as large as a forest, or as small as a pond.

Why Is Biodiversity Important?

Each species, no matter how small, has a role to play. A healthy community of diverse species will be able to sustain life. The species are better able to recover from natural disasters and changes in climate.

Our quality of life depends on biodiversity. We get many things from our environment. These include food products, timber, fresh water, clean air, and medicines. Healthy communities help regulate our climate and pollinate our crops. They also provide us with beautiful landscapes and recreational areas. By studying and maintaining biodiversity, we can help keep our planet healthy.

Brain Stretch

Sometimes areas become what is called a critical habitat. This happens when a species is threatened, or is near extinction, and needs protection. Laws have been written to prevent the killing, removal, or disturbance of species in protected critical habitats. This helps species survive and thrive.

Create a poster about a critical habitat near your community. Make sure to include information on what caused this area to become a critical habitat. Describe what is being done to help this area recover.

"Biodiversity"—Think About It!

1. In what way is the classification of organisms the same as the classification of habitats?

_____

_____

_____

2. The largest group of habitats is biomes. There are many types of biomes. Examples include deserts, forests, grasslands, tundra, and oceans. Choose a biome and create a brochure using the science brochure planner. Make sure your brochure has the following information on the biome: worldwide locations, climate, plants and animals, an example of a food chain, and interesting facts.

3. Canada has many forests. One type is the temperate deciduous forest. Most trees in these forests lose their leaves in winter. These forests experience four seasons, with cold winters and warm summers. Deciduous forests receive precipitation all year and have fertile soil. Think about what you know about forests like this. Do research to find out more. On a separate piece of paper, draw, then label, plants and animals you might find in a temperate deciduous forest. Include some non-living things in your drawing.

4. How is the community you live in similar to a habitat community?

_____

_____

_____

_____

_____

5. What do you think is the most important benefit humans get from biodiversity? Why?

_____

_____

_____

_____

_____

_____

Species Interactions

All organisms in a community have specific roles to play. Each species interacts with one or more other species. Most interactions involve competition for resources. Resources are things an organism needs to survive. These include food, water, sunlight, and shelter.

In a healthy community, there is a balance of organisms, so each one gets what it needs. An example is the food pyramid. There are more species and individuals at the bottom of the pyramid. There are fewer and fewer as you move up the pyramid. When a community works the way it should, there is a balance in the number of species at all levels.

example of a food pyramid

Symbiosis

Some organisms have a special relationship with other organisms. Symbiosis is a close relationship between two or more organisms. At least one organism receives a benefit from this relationship. There are three categories of symbiosis.

- **Mutualism**—Both organisms benefit from the relationship. One example is between a zebra and a bird called an oxpecker. The oxpecker eats ticks and other parasites that live on the zebra's skin. The oxpecker gets food, and the zebra benefits from having the pests removed.

- **Commensalism**—One organism benefits from the relationship and the other is not affected. One example is the remora. This fish has an adhesive disk on its head. The remora uses this to stick to a larger animal, such as a shark. When the shark is eating, scraps of food float away from the shark's mouth. The remora eats the scraps of food. The shark is not affected by the presence of the fish.

- **Parasitism**—One organism benefits from the relationship and the other is harmed in the process. One example is the flea. Fleas live on a host, such as a dog or cat. They bite their host's skin and suck their blood. The fleas get food and a warm home. But the host gets bitten repeatedly and is very itchy and uncomfortable.

"Species Interactions"—Think About It!

1. List these organisms in the order they would appear on a food pyramid, from bottom to top: mouse, corn, hawk, snake. Why would they be in this order?

_____

_____

_____

2. Read the following descriptions. Tell whether each gives an example of mutualism, commensalism, or parasitism. Give reasons to support your answer.

a) Burdock is a weed. The seed heads of the weed are burrs with hooked tips. These tips catch on cows, deer, or even people as they pass by. The burrs are dropped or brushed off in different places.

_____

_____

b) A certain type of bacteria lives in human intestines. This bacteria eats food that humans cannot digest, and partially digests the food. Then the human finishes digesting the food.

_____

_____

c) The deer tick attaches itself to an animal and feeds on the animal's blood.

_____

_____

3. Invasive species are organisms that are not naturally found in a community. They are usually brought in by people, sometimes for a reason and sometimes by accident. In 1998, zebra mussels were accidentally introduced into Lake St. Clair. They quickly spread throughout the Great Lakes and into many inland lakes, rivers, and canals. They have nearly eliminated the native clam population in the ecosystem. What effect can an invasive species have on a habitat community? Why?

_____

_____

_____

_____

Medicine from Plants

For thousands of years, people have relied on plants for food, building materials, and much more. One other very important way that plants help humans is by keeping them healthy.

Chemical Makers

Plants are able to make many chemicals that help them make food and grow. These chemical substances can also defend a plant against attacks from insects, fungi, and hungry animals. Scientists have been able to identify about 12,000 of these chemicals, but experts estimate that this is only about 10% of the total!

More than 120 of the chemical compounds used in modern medicine come from plants. People have known about the healing properties of plants' roots, leaves, flowers, bark, and berries since before written records were kept.

Bark and Leaves

The bark of the white willow contains a medicine that commonly known as aspirin. People have used it for pain relief for more than 2,000 years. Another important medicine, digitalis, comes from the foxglove plant. This chemical has been used since the 1500s to treat heart disease.

Malaria is an often fatal disease that is carried by mosquitoes. It kills thousands of people every year. The bark of the fever tree contains quinine, which is used to prevent and treat malaria. Another tropical plant, the aloe, has thick, fleshy leaves. The juice in these leaves contains alonin, a chemical that is used in medicine to cool burns, including sunburns.

aloe plant

More Help from Plants

Toothpick weed, or khella, is a herb from the area around the Mediterranean Sea. A chemical in this plant improves blood flow to the heart and helps the lungs work better. Scientists have used this plant to develop medicines to treat asthma and heart problems.

The Madagascar periwinkle has a small, bright-pink flower. This plant may alter the human immune system and is the source of a medicine used to treat diabetes and certain cancers. Meadow saffron also has a pinkish flower. But it is the bulb of this plant that has been used to treat rheumatism (painfully stiff arms, legs, and back) and gout (painful joints).

The rubber tree does not provide us with medicine, but it provides us with rubber to make such items as rubber gloves and waterproof sheeting that are important parts of health care and medicine.

Plants in Danger

As the plants in habitats around the world are being destroyed, thousands of possibly life-saving medicines are disappearing. Scientists believe that plants, especially those that grow in rain forests, may contain cures for some of the world's deadliest diseases.

"Medicine from Plants"—Think About It!

1. Match the plant to the drug it contains:

a) white willow tree   i) quinine

b) foxglove   ii) alonin

c) fever tree   iii) aspirin

d) aloe   iv) digitalis

2. How is the rubber tree different from the other plants mentioned in this article?

3. What are four ways that people have used plants? What are five plant parts people use?

4. People rely on plants. What does *rely* mean?

5. Why do people need to protect plants and where they live?

Adaptations

Organisms have characteristics that help them survive in their community. These adaptations can be physical structures or behaviours. Individuals with helpful traits are more likely to survive. They produce young with the same traits. Adaptations create biodiversity after many generations.

Structures

Physical features can help an organism survive. The beaks and feet of birds are good examples:

- short strong hooked beaks for eating animals
- long slender beaks to dig in mud for food
- webbed feet for swimming
- a long back toe to perch on branches

Structural adaptations can also be inside an animal. For example, a penguin's heart beats 60 to 100 times per minute. When the penguin dives, its heart rate drops to 20 beats per minute. That helps the penguin use less oxygen.

Behaviours

The things organisms do are called behaviours. They can help them find food or survive harsh weather. Hibernating and migrating are two behavioural adaptations. Hunting is another behaviour.

a change in colour is a type of adaptation

Yummy fish swim into the shade made by a snowy egret's wings. Nice catch!

Brain Stretch

Write about why adaptations are important for an animal's survival. Use information from the reading and your own ideas.

"Adaptations"—Think About It!

1. Choose two wild organisms—one plant and one animal. These organisms must live in your community habitat or another habitat that you know well. For each organism, describe one adaptation that helps the organism survive.

_____

_____

2. Read the descriptions below. For each, tell how the adaptation helps the organism survive.

   a) The American alligator digs a den in the mud in very hot weather.

   _____

   _____

   b) A beaver can close its lips behind its front teeth.

   _____

   _____

   c) The eyes of a hippopotamus are on top of its head.

   _____

   _____

3. Many organisms live in habitats that make survival difficult. These habitats include deserts, the Arctic, or the ocean floor. Design an imaginary organism that could survive in one of these habitats. Choose a habitat, then draw and label a picture of your organism below. Make sure your organism has adaptations that would help the organism survive. On another piece of paper, write a short paragraph to explain how the adaptations help the organism.

Cougars vs. Lynxes—What Is the Difference?

cougar   lynx

Cougars and lynxes are two of the biggest wildcats in North America. How are they alike? What is different about them?

Long Tails and Ear Tufts

The cougar is about the size of an adult human, and has a slim body, long tail, and silver- to reddish-coloured fur. It has a small round head with round ears. For its size, the cougar has the largest hind legs in the cat family.

Lynxes are well known for their long, black ear tufts. This wildcat is only about twice as large as a house cat. But, with its thick greyish-gold fur and full cheek tufts, it looks very solid and muscular.

Unlike cougars, lynxes have stubby little tails. These cats also differ in paw size. Despite their small body size, lynxes' paws are larger than human hands or feet. These huge paws act like snowshoes to help lynxes move around in the deep snow where they live.

Home and Hunting

Cougars have the largest range of any large wild land animal in North America. You can find these wildcats all the way from Canada's Yukon to the southern Andes Mountains in South America. But the lynx lives only in the forests and tundra of Canada, as well as the northern United States.

Both wildcats tend to live alone, although sometimes small groups of lynxes travel and hunt together. Cougars and lynxes hunt at night, climb well, and even swim, but the lynx is not a fast runner. When hunting, the lynx lies in wait for prey to come close, then pounces. The cougar is speedy over short distances, and can easily chase down prey.

Lynxes eat mostly snowshoe hares, but will also hunt small- to medium-sized animals and birds. Since cougars are much bigger, they eat animals as large as deer, elk, and moose. The cougar's powerful front legs and strong jaw help the cougar grasp and hold on to its dinner.

Shrieks, Purrs, and Hisses

The cougar is known for its blood-curdling screams, but cougars can also hiss, growl, and purr. A lynx has a call that sounds like a bark, and lynxes can also growl and wail.

Cougars actually do not make much noise, except perhaps when a female is calling to her babies. Cougar babies are born in dens located in caves or in shallow spaces on rocky cliffs. Female lynxes make a den to raise their babies in rock crevices, under rocky ledges, or beneath fallen trees.

1. Which is bigger, a cougar or a lynx? Which has the longer tail?

2. Are lynxes' paws larger or smaller than human hands?

3. How are the hunting styles of these two cats different?

4. Compare the animals that cougars and lynxes eat.

5. Female lynxes raise their babies in rock crevices. What is a *crevice*?

6. Why do you think these cats hunt at night?

Leafcutter Ants

Deep in the tropical rain forest lives an incredible insect. The leafcutter ant does not just gather food, it actually grows its own food in underground farms.

leafcutter ant

Millions of Ants

Leafcutter ants live in huge colonies of up to one million ants. They live in rain forests and tropical forests in Central America and South America, as well as southern areas of North America. They are large ants with long legs. Some leafcutter ants are orange, while others are brown, red, or black.

The nests where these ants live can be huge. The central mound may be more than 30 metres across. Smaller mounds around the main mound can be more than double that size and can increase the colony size to eight million ants. Humans are the only animal on Earth that forms larger, more complex societies than the leafcutter ant.

Tough and Strong

These ants crawl in long lines far into the forest to harvest leaves. To help them find their way back to their colonies, they leave a scent along the trail. With their strong jaws, leafcutter ants cut leaves from plants, then they carry these large leaf chunks over their backs. This strong insect can carry almost ten times its own weight.

Back in the colony, smaller ants chew the leaf chunks into a pulp. This pulp is stored with fungus spores in underground chambers. The ants also add their own droppings, which act like fertilizer, just as human farmers add manure to help their crops grow. Soon, strands of fungus begin to develop on the decaying pulp. The fungus is what the ants eat, not the leaves.

Careful Farmers

Leafcutter ants are able to sense the fungi's reaction to new plant material that is brought back to the colony. Scientists believe the insects pick up chemical signals from the fungus. For instance, if a particular type of leaf is deadly to the fungus, the leafcutter ants will detect this, quickly remove it, and stop collecting that kind of plant material.

Pest Control

In some areas where the leafcutter ants live, farmers consider them serious pests. Some of these insects can strip all the leaves off a citrus tree in less than 24 hours! Leafcutter ants also damage roads and farmland with their nest-building activity.

Farmers have found an interesting way to keep the ants away. The farmers collect debris and garbage from a leafcutter ant nest and place it around the crops or seedlings that they want to protect. That simple, environmentally friendly step keeps the leafcutter ants away for up to 30 days.

"Leafcutter Ants"—Think About It!

1. List the steps the leafcutter ant goes through to harvest leaves.

_____

_____

_____

_____

_____

2. Does the leafcutter ant have the most complex society on Earth? Give evidence from the text.

_____

_____

3. Strands of fungus develop on the decaying pulp in the ants' nest. What does *decaying* mean?

_____

_____

_____

4. List two reasons farmers consider leafcutter ants to be serious pests.

_____

_____

_____

5. How do farmers protect plants from leafcutter ants?

_____

_____

_____

Up in the Air

Orville and Wilbur Wright were the first men to build an airplane and make a controlled, powered flight. But the Wright brothers were not the first inventors to try to fly.

The Flying Sheep

As long ago as 1500, famous artist and inventor Leonardo da Vinci drew flying machines. These looked something like modern airplanes, but he never built any of them.

In 1783, Joseph and Étienne Montgolfier launched the world's first hot-air balloon in France. No one knew if the air was safe to breathe high above Earth's surface. So the brothers placed a duck, a rooster, and a sheep in a basket, tied the basket to the balloon, and sent it up.

When the balloon came back down, everyone was pleased that the animals had survived— although the sheep had stepped on the rooster. A few weeks later, the Montgolfiers successfully sent two men up in the balloon.

But the balloon could only drift where the wind blew it. Inventors wanted to create a flying machine that they could control.

Going for a Glide

Gliders were the next development in the attempt to invent a flying machine. The first one that could carry a person was launched in 1849. British inventor Sir George Cayley sent a 10-year-old boy up in a glider that carried him a short distance.

Cayley kept improving his designs. In 1854, he convinced his carriage driver to soar through the sky in his latest model. But it must have been a frightening experience: the man quit working for Cayley the second he was back on the ground! However, the inventor kept trying to build a glider that could be steered.

A Steerable Glider

The work Cayley did on gliders inspired inventor Otto Lilienthal. He built 16 models of gliders and, by 1896, had made 2,000 glider flights. This German inventor based his designs on what he had learned from watching birds soar through the sky.

Lilienthal became the first person to make repeated, successful gliding flights. He could steer his glider but, sadly, when he tried adding power to it, the machine crashed and Lilienthal was killed.

The Wrights Fly High

When the Wright brothers read about Lilienthal's achievements, they were inspired to build their own flying machine. Like the German inventor, they watched how birds flew, and that gave them ideas about how to steer. They started by building kites, then gliders. Finally, on December 17, 1903, they made the world's first controlled powered flight in an airplane they called the *Flyer.*

"Up in the Air"—Think About It!

1. Create a timeline of the events in this article.

_____

_____

_____

_____

_____

_____

_____

_____

2. Draw a picture showing the Montgolfiers' balloon in the air carrying a duck, rooster, and sheep.

"Up in the Air"—Think About It! (continued)

3. Orville and Wilbur Wright were the first men to make a controlled, powered flight. What does that mean?

4. Would you like to be an inventor? Give three reasons why or why not.

5. Where did some inventors of gliders and airplanes get their ideas for flight?

Flying Through the Sky

A car zooming along a road can move in just two different ways. A car can drive to the left or right and it can move up and down a hill. A plane can also tilt and twirl. Pilots use hinged flaps to change the shape of the plane in the air. This changes the aerodynamics and moves the plane. *Aerodynamics* is the study of air in motion.

The pilot can tilt the plane's nose up or down by tilting horizontal strips on the tail up or down.

Flaps on the wings tilt up and down to roll the plane.

A hinged rudder on the vertical tail makes the plane turn left or right.

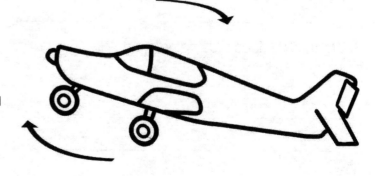

"Flying Through the Sky"—Think About It!

1. How does tilting a flap change the drag on a wing?

2. To go faster, should the flaps be flat or tilted? Explain why.

3. When a plane rolls, wind pushes up on one wing and down on the other wing. How does the pilot create these forces?

4. How could a bird change the tilt of its wings to slow down?

5. What force does the engine create?

Experiment: Build an Aircraft

What You Need

Materials such as:
- paper or plastic bags
- pipe cleaners, straws, craft sticks
- glue, tape, paper clips
- measuring tape, timer

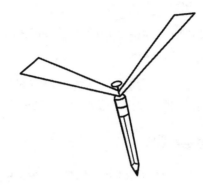

What You Do

1. Decide what type of aircraft you will build. For example, you might build an airplane, a spinner, or a glider.
2. Draw a plan and list the materials you need.
3. Decide how you will test the aircraft. Will you test the steering, time in the air, distance travelled, or all three?
4. Build the aircraft and conduct flight tests.
5. Record your findings.

Test	Flight Time	Distance Travelled	Steering
1			
2			
3			

Think About It!

1. Did your aircraft fly the way you thought it would? Explain.

_____

_____

2. What changes could make your aircraft fly better? Explain why.

_____

_____

_____

Aircraft with Motors

Amphibious Aircraft

Aircraft that can land and take off either on land or water are amphibious. Some have skis so they can also land on snow or ice. Amphibious aircraft are especially useful in remote areas where they can land on runways, lakes, or rivers.

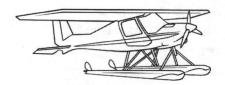

Helicopters

Helicopters get lift and thrust from the propellers—a rotor on the top. This rotor allows helicopters to take off and land vertically. It also lets the helicopter hover, and fly forward, backward, and sideways. Helicopters are often used in areas where there is no room for an airplane runway.

Stealth Planes

Stealth aircraft are military aircraft. These planes use advanced technology to avoid being detected by radar. Stealth planes have features that interfere with radar. These features make the plane difficult to see, hear, or detect with hi-tech equipment. However, these aircraft can be detected when they use their weapons. Stealth planes can have human pilots. They can also be flown by remote control.

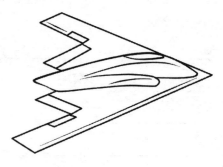

Think About It!

1. People are searching for a hiker lost in the wilderness. Give three reasons it would be better to search with a helicopter than with an airplane.

_____

_____

_____

_____

Animal Fliers

You have learned a lot about machines that fly. Many animals can fly too. Some have wings. Some have feathers. Others stretch skin into a wing shape.

Insects

Insects are amazing fliers because they can turn their wings. That lets them hover in the air or even fly backward. Spiders coast through the air on silky lines that catch the wind.

Bats

bat

When you look at a bat's wing, you may see long bony fingers with a thin skin or membrane stretched between them. Bats flap their spread-out fingers to fly.

Birds

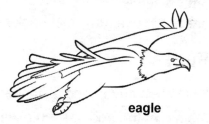

eagle

Birds flap their wings to propel them through the air. They change the shape and angle of their wings to take off, steer, and land. Some birds are excellent gliders and barely flap their wings.

Think About It!

1. Animals that fly have very light skeletons. An animal of similar size that does not fly is much heavier. How does a light skeleton help a flying animal?

_____

_____

_____

_____

2. List a reason each of the following is able to fly:

Insects: _____

Bats: _____

Birds: _____

Furred and Finned Fliers

Squirrels

A flying squirrel can not really fly, but it is an excellent glider. It can coast farther than the length of three hockey rinks! First, a flying squirrel opens up a flap of furry skin that stretches from each wrist to each ankle. Then it glides with its body spread out. Its tail is puffed out so it works like a parachute.

flying squirrel

Reptiles

When a flying lizard unfurls its wings, it is easy to see the ribs that support the wings. The ribs and attached membrane spread out to form a semicircle on each side of the lizard's body. When these wings are not in use, they fold back against the animal's sides.

flying lizard

Fish

Flying fish cover long distances by making a series of glides through the air. At the end of each glide, a flying fish dips its tail into the water. This action produces new forward thrust. Flying squid propel themselves out of the water by expelling water. These creatures usually glide through the air only when they need to escape predators.

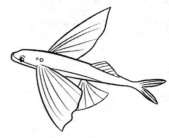

flying fish

Other Fliers

It is not only animals that use wings and air currents to get around. Dandelion seeds use their fluff like a parachute to float to new environments. Maple keys spin through the air like a helicopter or fall slowly. This helps them move away from the tree where they were produced.

Think About It!

1. Imagine a toy that would fly like an animal. What design features should it have? List two things.

_____

_____

_____

_____

Amelia Earhart

Amelia Earhart was an American aviator who broke many flying records. Today, she is even more famous for vanishing … without a trace.

Up in the Air

This high flyer was born in 1897 in Kansas in the United States. When she finished high school, Amelia was not sure what she wanted to do. So she worked as a nurse and decided she would study medicine. But that all changed when she took her first ride in a plane. As soon as the plane was just a short way off the ground, Amelia knew that she had to learn to fly.

The Canary

When Amelia was back on the ground, she immediately began working hard to earn enough money to pay for flying lessons. Eventually, she bought her own plane. It was bright yellow, so she called it "The Canary." Amelia soon had her pilot's licence and was ready to fly.

In 1928, Amelia was asked to take part in a flight across the Atlantic Ocean from the United States to Wales in Great Britain. Flying with a pilot and co-pilot, Amelia was the navigator. She was the first woman to be carried by plane across the Atlantic. She returned to the United States a hero, although she did not think she deserved all the attention she received. Instead, she became determined to fly across the ocean by herself.

Across the Atlantic

In 1932, Amelia took off from Harbour Grace, Newfoundland. It was not long before she ran into bad weather and thick clouds. Her windshield and wings were often covered with ice.

Amelia was aiming for Paris, but she had to cut her flight short and land in Northern Ireland instead. However, she became the first woman to pilot a plane solo across the Atlantic Ocean. Only one man, Charles Lindbergh, had successfully flown solo across the ocean before her.

Vanished!

Amelia was the most famous woman in the world, but she still was not satisfied. She wanted to be the first woman to fly all around the world. So, in June 1937, she and her navigator, Fred Noonan, took off from Miami, Florida.

Planes could not fly as far back then, so they had to make a number of stops. First, the pair flew to Puerto Rico, then east to Africa. They flew to Pakistan, then India, and soon were in New Guinea in the south Pacific Ocean.

On July 2, Amelia and Fred took off to fly to Howland Island in the Pacific Ocean. They were never seen again. No trace has ever been found of this brave pilot or her plane, and her final flight remains a mystery.

"Amelia Earhart"—Think About It!

1. What is the main idea of this article?

_____

_____

_____

_____

2. What accomplishments made Earhart the most famous woman in the world?

_____

_____

_____

3. Do you like to fly? Give three reasons why or why not.

_____

_____

_____

4. Earhart did not think she deserved all the attention she received. What does this mean and what does it tell you about her personality?

_____

_____

_____

_____

5. What do you think happened to Earhart? Give three reasons for your conclusion.

_____

_____

_____

_____

6. On a separate piece of paper, write a news article detailing Amelia Earhart's accomplishments and her disappearance. Use information from the text and other research tools for your article.

Article Checklist

Content

☐ An attention-grabbing headline names the article.

☐ The byline shows my name as the author.

☐ The beginning gives the most important facts.

☐ The middle gives supporting details about the main idea.

☐ The ending gives the reader an idea to remember.

Grammar and Style

☐ I used my neatest printing and included a clear headline.

☐ I included a colourful picture to support my article.

☐ I used descriptive language.

☐ I checked the spelling.

☐ I checked the punctuation.

Current and Static Electricity

Static Electricity

Pull a wool hat off and your hair tries to stand on end. Walk across a carpet and you may get a shock when you touch something. Why does this happen?

When objects rub, a charge builds up on the surface. The charge can be positive or negative, like the poles on a battery. You cannot see the charge on an object, but you might see what the charge does. The charge makes hairs stand up and balloons stick to walls. The charge can also make a stream of water bend toward the charge.

Because the charge stays in place for a while, we call this charge static electricity. When the charge moves from one object to another, you may see—and feel—the spark.

Current Electricity

Current electricity flows along a path of electricity called a circuit. A circuit connects the source of a electricity to a load that does something useful. The source might be a power plant, or it might be a battery. A light bulb is one type of load.

Think About It!

1. Circle the examples that use current electricity.

    shock from walking on carpet   **flashlight**   **lightning**

    power lines in a house   **solar calculator**   **light switch**

2. Items with the same charge push apart from each other. Items with opposite charges are attracted to each other. Do these items have the same charge or opposite?

    a) A balloon sticks to a wall. _____

    b) Hairs push away from each other so hard that they stand straight up. _____

3. When clothes come out of the dryer, some may stick together. We call this "static cling" because static electricity causes the clothing to cling. Explain what happens to make the clothes stick together.

    _____

    _____

Experiment: Electric Cereal

Try this experiment to see static electricity at work.

What You Need

- Hard plastic comb
- Liquid soap
- Dish towel or paper towel
- 30 cm of thread
- Piece of dry O-shaped cereal
- Wool mitten or sock
- Table
- Tape
- Balloon (optional)

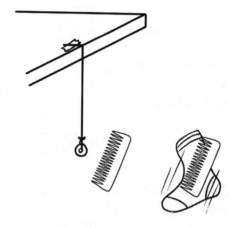

What You Do

1. Tie one end of the thread to a piece of cereal.
2. Tape the other end of the thread to the top of a table, so the cereal hangs in the air. The cereal should not be too close to anything.
3. Wash the comb with soap to make sure there is no oil on the comb. Carefully rinse away all of the soap. Dry the comb with the towel. (Make sure the comb is completely dry.)
4. Rub the comb quickly on the wool for several moments.
5. a) *Slowly* bring the comb close to the cereal. Do not touch the comb to the cereal. At a certain point, the cereal should move. Record what happens.
   b) Hold the comb still until the cereal moves again. Note how the cereal moves this time.
6. Once again, slowly bring the comb closer to the cereal. See if you can make the comb touch the cereal. Record what happens.

Optional

7. If a balloon is available, blow the balloon up and tie off the end. Repeat steps 4 through 6, using the balloon instead of the comb. Note any differences in the results.

"Experiment: Electric Cereal"—Think About It!

1. Record the results of your experiment in the chart below. Use drawings or words.

What I Did	What I Saw
Slowly moved the comb close to the cereal **(Step 5 a)**	
Held the comb still until the cereal moved again **(Step 5 b)**	
Tried to touch the comb to the cereal **(Step 6)**	

2. How does the comb become electrified?

____

____

3. Is this an example of static electricity or current electricity? Explain.

____

____

4. Did the comb and wool cause the effect you saw? Did the cereal cause the effect you saw? Describe a step you could add to test this.

____

____

Using Water to Produce Electricity

Hydro means "water." Hydroelectric power plants use water to create electricity.

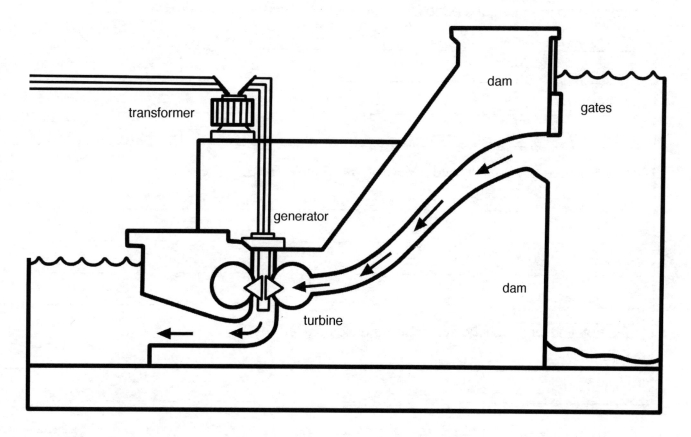

How It Works

1. A dam is built in a river. Water collects behind the dam, creating a lake or reservoir.

2. When the gates are open, water rushes down a pipe to the turbines.

3. The water turns the turbine blades, which turns the rod the blades are attached to.

4. The turbine makes the rod and magnets spin very quickly inside the generator. As the magnets spin, charge builds up in coils of copper wire, creating electricity.

5. The electricity travels along wires to the transformer. The transformer can help send electricity far away to where electrical power is needed.

"Using Water to Produce Electricity"—Think About It!

1. Explain how each group might feel about a hydroelectric dam being built.

a) People who live along the edge of the river where the lake will be created

_____

_____

_____

_____

b) People who enjoy boating and waterskiing

_____

_____

_____

_____

c) Unemployed workers who live near the building site

_____

_____

_____

_____

d) People who believe that an earthquake might happen where the dam will be built

_____

_____

_____

_____

2. If you lived close to the site of the proposed dam, how would you feel about the dam? Explain why.

_____

_____

_____

Using Wind to Produce Electricity

People have used wind power for centuries. Early windmills turned grinding stones that crushed grain into flour. Today we use windmills to create electricity.

How Wind Turbines Work

You can think of a wind turbine as the opposite of a fan. A fan uses electricity to make its blades turn, and the turning blades produce moving air. A wind turbine uses moving air (wind) to turn its blades. The movement of the blades produces electricity.

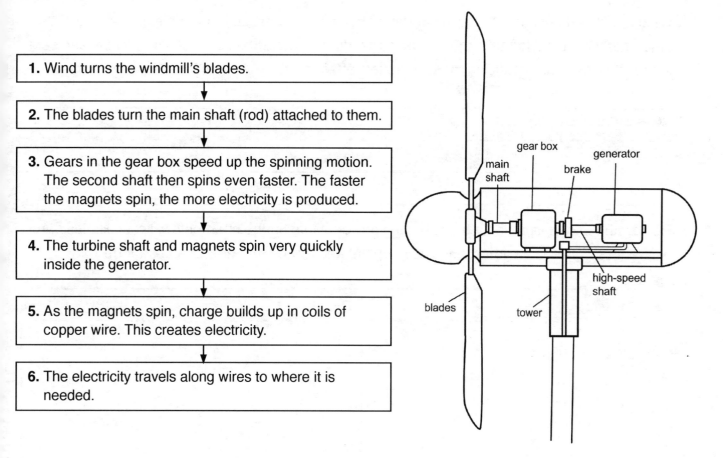

1. Wind turns the windmill's blades.

2. The blades turn the main shaft (rod) attached to them.

3. Gears in the gear box speed up the spinning motion. The second shaft then spins even faster. The faster the magnets spin, the more electricity is produced.

4. The turbine shaft and magnets spin very quickly inside the generator.

5. As the magnets spin, charge builds up in coils of copper wire. This creates electricity.

6. The electricity travels along wires to where it is needed.

Wind Farms

A wind farm is a place that has a lot of wind turbines. The area must be flat and open, with a lot of wind. A wind farm can be built over water, such as a lake or ocean.

Advantages of Wind Turbines	Disadvantages of Wind Turbines
• create electricity • do not create pollution • many possible locations	• noisy • can be seen from quite far away • turning blades can kill or injure birds and bats

"Using Wind to Produce Electricity"—Think About It!

1. Why should wind turbine blades be very lightweight?

2. Wind turbines do not pollute the environment when they operate. But the metal, concrete, and other materials used to make them must be produced. The turbines must also be built and sent to the site. How can producing these materials affect the environment?

3. Review the information about hydroelectric power plants. In the chart below, list similarities and differences between a hydroelectric power plant and a wind turbine. (Use point form.)

Similarities	Differences

Our Sun Is a Star

Earth circles around the Sun. The Sun is a star and we could not live without it. The Sun is a ball of burning gas that gives us light and heat. The light makes plants grow, which provides us with food and with oxygen to breathe. The Sun's heat gives us rain by warming oceans and lakes. When that happens, some of the water evaporates into water vapour, which floats into the sky. When the water vapour rises high enough, it hits cooler air and condenses, and eventually falls as rain.

How big is the Sun? If the Sun were a hollow ball, one million Earths would fit inside it.

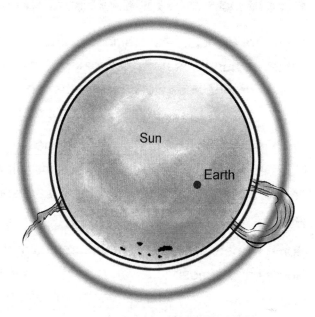

One million Earths could fit inside the Sun. The Sun has 333,000 times the mass of Earth.

Other Stars

Like the Sun, all stars are balls of burning gas. But stars are not all the same size and colour. Stars can be 40 times larger than our Sun, or almost as small as Earth. Blue stars are very hot, while red stars are much cooler. In between are white and yellow stars. Our Sun is known as a yellow dwarf star.

The Sun seems larger than other stars in the sky because it is closer to us than any other star. Some stars are so far away that their light takes more than 1,000 years to reach Earth.

Think About It!

1. In what ways does the Sun affect Earth? Use the information from the article and your own ideas to write your answer.

_____

_____

SAFETY ALERT

Never look at the Sun! Even when you wear sunglasses, sunlight can damage your eyes.

Brain Stretch

All stars have a life cycle. Do some research to find out about the stages in the life cycle of a star. Create an information poster that includes diagrams and labels.

Planets in Our Solar System

There are eight planets orbiting our Sun. Each planet orbits the Sun on its own path. The planets' paths are hundreds of millions of kilometres apart. At any point in time, the planets are usually at very different places along their paths. So, the distance between planets is even greater. Earth is so far from the Sun that the Sun's light takes eight minutes to reach our planet.

Each planet spins around as it orbits the Sun. On Earth, this creates night and day, as different sides of the planet get sunlight. The time it takes for a planet to orbit the Sun is one year. Earth's year is 365 days long. Some planets have shorter years than Earth and some have much longer years.

Some planets have moons and some have rings. Some have atmosphere, winds, and storms. Huge craters, mountains, and canyons can be seen on some planets. Match each planet shown in the illustration to a description below.

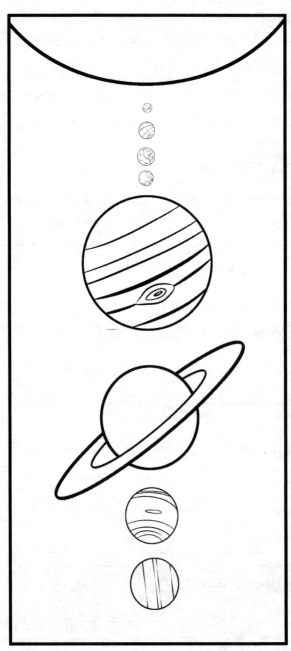

Mercury

Mercury is the closest planet to the Sun and is the smallest planet in our solar system. The surface is grey and rocky and has a lot of craters. With almost no atmosphere, it does not have storms, clouds, winds, or rain. With no atmosphere to trap the daytime heat, the temperature can drop 600°C from day to night. No other planet has such an extreme temperature range.

Venus

Venus is about the size of Earth. The temperature on the surface is hot enough to melt lead. In fact, no planet is hotter than Venus. Not even Mercury, which is the planet closest to the Sun. Mercury and Venus are the only two planets that do not have moons orbiting them. Venus is easy to see. It reflects the Sun's light so brightly that some people mistake it for a star.

Earth

From space, Earth looks blue. That is because oceans cover 70% of Earth's surface. Earth is the third planet from the Sun and the largest of the four rocky planets. It is the densest planet. Earth spins on a tilt as it orbits the Sun. This tilt means that half the planet gets more solar energy than the other half. This tilt is the reason Earth has changing seasons.

Mars

Iron in the soil gives the planet a reddish colour. Huge dust storms can almost cover the planet. Mars is about half the size of Earth, but has the highest mountain and the largest canyon of any planet. Space probes have looked for life on Mars, but found none. But scientists think the planet may once have been covered in rivers and oceans.

Jupiter

Jupiter is called a gas giant. This planet is so big that all other planets could fit inside it. Jupiter has at least 64 moons—more than any other planet. One moon is larger than Mercury. Jupiter is the fifth planet from the Sun, but can be seen easily from Earth. A space probe showed that Jupiter is circled by faint dark rings made of dust and bits of rock.

Saturn

No other planet has rings so bright. These rings are made of pieces of dust, rock, and ice. Some are as small as a fingernail, others are as big as a house. Some experts think the rings contains materials left over from when Saturn formed. Others think the rings contain pieces of nearby moons, chipped off by meteorites.

Uranus

Uranus is the only planet tilted on its side. Some experts think it may once have been hit by something huge that knocked it on its side. The planet is the third-largest in our solar system and is surrounded by faint rings. Unlike other planets, it has no cloud bands or storms. Uranus is so far from the Sun that sunlight on Earth is 400 times brighter than the sunlight on Uranus.

Neptune

Neptune is a giant blue ball with wisps of white clouds. The winds blow up to 2,000 km/h on Neptune. No other planet has faster winds. Neptune is about the same size as Uranus and is the second-farthest planet from the Sun. There are four seasons on Neptune, but each season lasts more than 40 Earth years.

"Planets in Our Solar System"—Think About It!

1. Mars has two moons: Phobos and Deimos. How many moons do the four planets closest to the Sun have all together? _____

2. Which planet has the highest-known mountain? _____

3. Which planet is the hottest? _____

4. Which planet is the smallest? _____

5. Which planet is the largest? _____

6. Which planet is the densest? _____

7. Which planet has the greatest daily temperature change? _____

8. Which planet spins on its side? _____

9. Imagine the Sun is the size of a basketball. Now match each planet with an item about its size. (Hint: three pairs of planets are about the same size as each other. For instance, Venus is almost the same size as Earth.)

   a) Mercury   i) small number cube
   b) Venus   ii) gum ball
   c) Earth   iii) peppercorn
   d) Mars   iv) large marble
   e) Jupiter   v) black bean
   f) Saturn   vi) kernel of corn
   g) Uranus   vii) pea
   h) Neptune   viii) small marble

Brain Stretch

Here is the order of the planets, starting with the planet closest to the Sun: Mercury, Venus, Earth, Mars, Jupiter, Saturn, Uranus, Neptune. The sentence below can help you remember the order of the planets. The first letter of each word is the first letter of a planet.

My Very Efficient Mother Just Served Us Noodles.

Moons

Did you know there are likely about 140 moons in our solar system? Jupiter has more than 64 moons. Mercury and Venus are the only planets that do not have a moon.

A moon can be any size. Two moons in our solar system are even bigger than Mercury. The second-largest moon is Titan, which orbits Saturn. Scientists are very interested in Titan because its atmosphere seems similar to Earth's long ago. Could there be life there now or some time in the future?

Our Moon is about one quarter the size of Earth. The surface is covered with boulders and a thick layer of grey dust. There are many large craters and mountain ranges, but no atmosphere. Millions of asteroids, comets, and meteorites have scarred the Moon's surface. There is no wind or rain to wash away these marks, so they remain unchanged for years.

The Moon Affects Life on Earth

The Moon circles Earth, reflecting light from the Sun and pulling on Earth's oceans. Ocean tides are caused by the Moon's gravity pulling the water toward the Moon. Since Earth rotates as this happens, two tides happen every day.

A lunar eclipse occurs when Earth comes between the Sun and the Moon. Earth's shadow makes the whole Moon look red and mysterious.

The Sun and Moon must be exactly opposite each other for a total eclipse. Partial eclipses happen much more often. A few lunar eclipses happen each year. Most can only be seen from certain places on Earth, depending on where the darkest shadow passes.

Phases of the Moon

Do you ever wonder why the Moon looks so bright in the night sky? Earth's Moon is not a star, yet it gives off its own light. This is because the surface of the Moon reflects the light from the Sun. The part of the Moon facing the Sun is lit up. The part of the Moon facing away from the Sun is dark. The sunlit part of the moon that we see is what is responsible for the Moon's phases. The phases of the Moon depend on its position in relation to the Sun and Earth. As the Moon makes its way around the Earth, the phases of the Moon change.

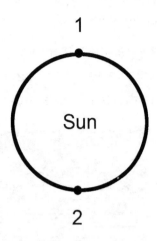

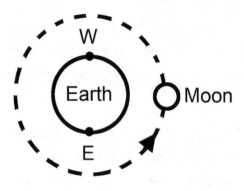

1. Draw a lunar eclipse. On the diagram above, use one colour to join point 1 to points E and W. Extend the lines to the Moon. Colour between the lines. Use another colour to join point 2 to points E and W. Extend the lines to the Moon and colour in the shape. Look at the shadow you coloured between Earth and the Moon. The area of mixed colour is the location of the darkest shadow.

2. Look at the Moon every few nights for about a month. Look in the newspaper to find out what time the Moon rises each night. Note what you see.

   a) The Moon does not actually change shape. Why does what you see change?

   _____

   _____

   b) Number the moon pictures below in the order that you saw them.

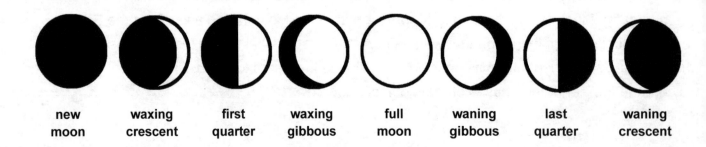

| new moon | waxing crescent | first quarter | waxing gibbous | full moon | waning gibbous | last quarter | waning crescent |

They Came from Outer Space

Comets

You might say a comet is a dirty snowball that orbits the Sun. This snowball is about the size of a small city! As this snowball zooms closer to the Sun, its surface begins to turn into gas. Gas and dust stream out into a tail that can spread out as far as 80,000 km.

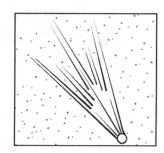

Comets mostly stay farther away from the Sun than our planets are. You will rarely see a comet unless you use a telescope or binoculars. Halley's Comet is the most famous comet. It swings by Earth about every 75 years. You will have to wait until 2062 to see it again.

Asteroids

These space rocks may be shaped like balls, lumpy slabs, or bricks. You find asteroids circling the Sun in the Asteroid Belt, a band that lies between the planets Mars and Jupiter.

The biggest asteroid is bigger than many Canadian provinces. One asteroid even has its own moon. Most asteroids are only about the size of a house. You need binoculars to seem them.

Meteoroids

Small chunks of asteroids or old comets may become meteoroids. When these rocky bits enter Earth's atmosphere, they become meteors. Ever seen shooting stars? Then you have seen meteors. They burn up and shoot out fiery trails as they fall. If a meteor hits our planet, it gets a new name: meteorite.

Meteors are tiny. Most are as small as grains of sand and few get as big as baseballs. At certain times of year, many meteors streak through the night sky in a meteor shower. You can see them just by gazing up on a clear, dark night.

Think About It!

1. Arrange these in order of size: asteroid, meteoroid, comet.

_____

2. Name one meteor shower and explain its name.

_____

_____

Astronauts and Space Travel

In space you do not feel gravity. It is extremely cold, and there is no atmosphere to breathe or to protect you from the Sun's radiation. It takes enormous energy to get there, and you have to take everything you need with you—even the air. Outer space is an extreme environment.

The first person in space orbited Earth for less than two hours in 1957. Less than 40 years later, another astronaut spent a record-setting 438 days in space. Space travel has changed a lot since then. Between 1969 and 1972, 12 astronauts set foot on the Moon. These are the only times a human has landed anywhere other than Earth.

After leaving Earth, life support is the most important function of a spacecraft. It must clean the air for astronauts to breathe and provide heat. It must also protect the contents from X-rays and other radiation coming from the Sun. All things used in space are designed with the low gravity in mind. Tools are attached to surfaces so they do not float away. Even drinking becomes difficult. You do not think about it, but gravity keeps the drink in your glass. Without gravity, the drink floats in a ball. Meals must be eaten from containers that keep the food from floating away. Equipment must be protected from floating crumbs too.

Gravity on Earth also makes your muscles work hard. This exercise helps the blood spread throughout your body. In space, blood does not circulate as well. Lack of exercise makes the body lose muscle and bone mass. Astronauts have to strap themselves into exercise equipment to keep from floating away!

Brain Stretch

What do you think are four character traits someone needs to have to become an astronaut? Justify your thinking for each character trait.

_____

_____

_____

_____

"Astronauts and Space Travel"—Think About It!

1. List 10 items you would need in space. Give a reason you want to take each item.

_____

_____

_____

_____

_____

_____

_____

_____

_____

2. What are the most important features to have on a spacecraft? Remember, the spacecraft has to provide everything an astronaut will need while in space.

_____

_____

_____

_____

_____

Brain Stretch

Some of the things we use on Earth were invented for space travel. Heat cameras, insulation, multivitamins, and cordless tools are just a few examples. Use books or Internet resources to learn about one such invention. Create a demonstration to show people how to use it on Earth.

Space Technology

Space travel has changed your life in ways you probably never imagined. From your sunglasses to the shoes you wear hiking, space technology touches your life.

How were these devices first used in

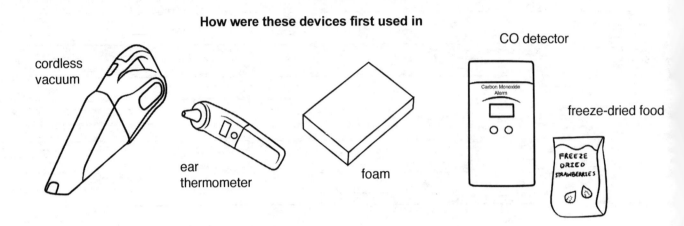

cordless vacuum

ear thermometer

foam

CO detector

Carbon Monoxide Alarm

freeze-dried food

FREEZE DRIED STRAWBERRIES

You likely already know that radio and television signals are transmitted around our planet by satellite. Other satellites help with navigation. Many cars now have global positioning systems (GPS), which are navigation systems that use satellites. Other products include the scratchproof coating on sunglasses, and medical technology. Insulin crystals (to fight diabetes) were grown in space. The technology used for space shuttle fuel pumps is now used in artificial hearts.

Space technology is great, but it costs a lot. It takes an incredible amount of money to put an astronaut into space. It costs $19 million just for a toilet on the International Space Station! Also, astronauts' dirty clothes cannot be cleaned, so these expensive garments are just thrown away. Is this the best way for a government to spend its money?

Here on Earth, money is desperately needed to improve medical care and other services. We also need more money to help the environment. Is it right to spend money on space research when the money is needed elsewhere? Are space programs just a way for one country to pretend it is better than another because it has more advanced space technology?

Space travel also creates a lot of pollution. Launching a spacecraft uses a lot of fuel. On Earth, people are trying to save fuel. Space research also adds to the garbage orbiting Earth or eventually landing on our planet. Some pieces are as large as a car. Even bits as small as flecks of paint can damage other spacecraft because of the speeds at which they travel.

The worst outcome of space research can be disastrous. Although every aspect is carefully planned, sometimes tragedies happen. In 1986, the Space Shuttle *Challenger* blew up shortly after takeoff. Then in 2003, the shuttle *Columbia* broke apart as it re-entered Earth's atmosphere. In both cases, all seven crew members were killed.

1. How do you feel about space technology and exploration? What are the benefits? Do the benefits outweigh the costs? Do you think life on Earth would be better or worse without space travel? Write a paragraph to express your thoughts.

_____

_____

_____

_____

_____

2. Space technology has changed the foods we eat. There are six main ways food is stored for astronauts to eat on board the space shuttle. Match each method with its description.

a) Fresh

b) Intermediate Moisture

c) Irradiated

d) Natural

e) Rehydratable

f) Thermostabilized

i) Food is freeze-dried to remove water. Water is replaced before eating.

ii) Food has some water removed; water is not replaced before eating.

iii) Food is cooked and packed in foil pouches. The food is sterilized by radiation so it can be kept at room temperature.

iv) Food is heated to kill bacteria so it can be stored at room temperature.

v) Food is ready to eat and stored in flexible pouches.

vi) Food is not preserved, so it must be eaten quickly.

3. Imagine exploring the ocean in a submarine. How is this similar to life in space?

_____

_____

_____

_____

_____

It Came from Space

Space exploration is very new in the history of humankind. Space travel began in 1957, when the first artificial satellite was launched by the Soviet Union. Yuri Gagarin became the first person to orbit Earth in 1961. In 1962, Alan Shepard became the first American to do the same thing. In 1969, Neil Armstrong became the first person to walk on the Moon.

Since then, space exploration has advanced very rapidly, and it has produced a large amount of amazing technology that we take for granted today. Technologies originally developed for use in space have found new and sometimes unexpected uses on Earth, in products called *spinoffs*. Here are just a few of the products we owe to space exploration:

Invisible Braces: A new material was developed to help track heat-seeking missiles. This new material is now used to make invisible braces.

Coatings for Lenses: A special coating was developed to protect plastic space equipment, such as visors for astronauts. This coating is used today to make plastic lenses that are very hard to scratch.

Smoke Detectors: Smoke detectors like the ones you use in your home were developed to detect fire or gases in Skylab, the first space station.

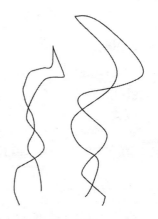

Cordless Tools: Lightweight, cordless tools were developed to help astronauts collect mineral and rock samples from the Moon.

CAT and MRI Scans: A technology was developed to photograph the Moon's surface and find a good place to land. CAT and MRI technologies were developed from this. They are used today in hospitals all around the world to produce images of the insides of people's bodies.

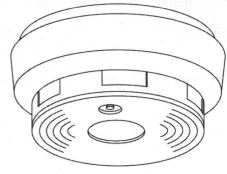

Memory Foam: A special foam was developed to protect astronauts from impact when landing. This foam is now used in many places, such as airline seats, pillows, mattresses, and cushions for wheelchairs.

A smoke detector

Blood Analysis Machine: Technology was developed to create a compact lab instrument that analyzes blood in 30 seconds rather than 20 minutes. This is used by doctors and hospitals today.

All of these technologies and many more help make our lives better.

"It Came from Space"—Think About It!

1. Why does the author say that space exploration is new in the history of humankind?

_____

_____

_____

2. When or why might it be important to do a blood analysis in 30 seconds?

_____

_____

3. What do you think the word *spinoff* means as used in this text? Why is this a good word for the technologies discussed in the text?

_____

_____

_____

4. The Moon is a satellite that orbits (goes around) Earth. What do you think an *artificial satellite* is?

_____

_____

_____

5. What is the main idea of this text? How does the author support the main idea?

_____

_____

_____

6. How does the author feel about these technologies? Use specific details from the text to support your answer.

_____

_____

_____

On the Job with an Iceberg Wrangler

My name is Dan. I am a Marine Surface Manager, but most people call me an iceberg wrangler. That means that if an iceberg looks as though it might crash into an oil rig, my crew and I move it out of the way. Come aboard my ship and find out about my workday!

9 a.m.

We got a call last night that an iceberg was headed for an exploration rig out in Iceberg Alley. That is the area off the east coast of Newfoundland where icebergs float down from Baffin Bay on the Labrador Current.

As soon as we heard there could be a problem with an iceberg, we headed out to sea. These days, there are lots of people keeping an eye on icebergs. The International Ice Patrol was formed more than 100 years ago, just after an iceberg sank the Titanic. Today, iceberg watchers track icebergs by using satellite and radar technology, information from airplanes and helicopters, and information about ocean currents, weather, and wind.

1 p.m.

We can see the iceberg now and we decide that it is towable. Most of them are. It is not too rounded, so the rope will not slip off while it is being towed. First, we attach a thick rope to a buoy, then we circle the iceberg, letting the rope out as we go. When we get back to the buoy, we connect up a tow cable to the first rope, then begin to pull. We do not actually tow the iceberg—most are too big for that—but we change the angle which it is drifting.

4 p.m.

Some of the crew and I take a quick break for an early dinner. One of them starts talking about an iceberg we had to move last week that had a very strange shape.

I knew it would be difficult to tow, so I decided to use our water cannon on it. Imagine a really powerful fire hose directed right at the iceberg. The pressure of the water pushed the iceberg in a new direction, away from a possibly dangerous collision.

Did You Know?

- A lot of people say icebergs smell like cucumbers.
- The largest iceberg ever recorded in the Northern Hemisphere weighed more than 9 billion tonnes.

When I first started out in this job, we often used the force of the water from the boat's propellers to move icebergs. We had to back up close to the iceberg, then gun the engines so the boat's propeller wash hit the iceberg. This took a long time because we had to keep going back and forth and back and forth, so this is not done very often anymore.

"Iceberg Wrangler"—Think About It!

1. Where is Iceberg Alley?

_____

_____

2. What are two methods iceberg wranglers use to move icebergs?

_____

_____

3. Why is it important to move icebergs out of the way of rigs and ships?

_____

_____

4. Iceberg wranglers sometimes use the pressure of water from a water cannon to move icebergs. What does *pressure* mean?

_____

_____

_____

5. Would you like to be an iceberg wrangler? Explain your thinking.

_____

_____

_____

6. What does this text remind you of?

_____

_____

_____

STEM-Related Occupations

To learn more about some of these occupations visit the following websites:

http://www.sciencebuddies.org/science-fair-projects/science_careers.shtml

http://kids.usa.gov/watch-videos/jobs/index.shtml

https://canada2067.ca/en/

http://www.scouts.ca/program/stem/

Accountant
Aerospace Engineer
Agricultural Engineer
Agricultural Technician
Aircraft Mechanic and
    Service Technician
Animal Breeder
Animal Trainer
Animator
Anthropologist
Architect
Astronaut
Astronomer
Athletic Trainer
Audio Engineer
Audiologist
Automotive Mechanic
Biochemical Engineer
Biochemist/Biophysicist
Biologist
Biology Teacher
Biomedical Engineer
Business Owner
Cardiovascular Technician
Carpenter
Chef
Chemical Engineer
Chemical Technician
Chemistry Teacher
Chiropractor
Civil Engineer
Civil Engineering Technician
Climate Change Analyst
Clinical Psychologist
Computer Engineer
Computer Programmer
Computer Systems Analyst
Construction Manager
Counselling Psychologist
Dietetic Technician

Dietitian and Nutritionist
Doctor
Electrical Engineering Technician
Electrician
Electronics Engineer
Emergency Medical Technician
Environmental Engineer
Environmental Engineering Technician
Environmental Restoration Planner
Environmental Scientist
Epidemiologist
Fire-Prevention Engineer
Fish and Game Worker
Food Science Technician
Food Scientist and Technologist
Forest and Conservation Technician
Forest and Conservation Worker
Geoscientist
Graphic Designer
Hydrologist
Industrial Engineer
Interior Designer
Landscape Architect
Manufacturing Engineer
Marine Architect
Marine Biologist
Math Teacher
Mechanical Engineer
Mechanical Engineering Technician
Medical Lab Technician
Medical Scientist
Meteorologist
Microbiologist
Microsystems Engineer
Mining and Geological Engineer
Molecular and Cellular Biologist
Neurologist
Nuclear Engineer
Nursery and Greenhouse Manager

Nutritionist
Occupational Health and Safety Specialist
Optical Engineer
Optometrist
Paleontologist
Patent Lawyer
Pathologist
Park Ranger
Petroleum Engineer
Pharmacist
Physical Therapist
Physician
Physician Assistant
Physicist
Pilot
Psychologist
Registered Nurse
Respiratory Therapist
Robotics Engineer or Technician
School Psychologist
Seismologist
Software Developer (Applications)
Software Developer (Systems Software)
Soil and Plant Scientist
Soil and Water Conservationist
Space Scientist
Speech-Language Pathologist
Statistician
Transportation Engineer
Transportation Planner
Urban Planner
Veterinarian
Video Game Designer
Volcanologist
Water/Wastewater Engineer
Wind Energy Engineer
X-ray Technician
Zookeeper
Zoologist and Wildlife Biologist

Science, Technology, Engineering, and Mathematics (STEM) Occupation Brochure

Create a brochure about a STEM-related occupation.

STEP 1: Plan Your Brochure

☐ Take a piece of paper and fold the paper the same way your brochure will be folded. Before writing the brochure, plan the layout in pencil. Sections of the brochure should include:
- Job description
- Training or degree needed
- Work environment
- How the occupation relates to STEM
- Interesting facts

☐ Write the heading for each section where you would like it to be in the brochure.

☐ Plan where graphics or pictures will be placed in the brochure.

STEP 2: Complete a Draft

☐ Research information for each section of your brochure. Check your facts.

☐ Read your draft for meaning, then add, delete, or change words to make your writing better.

☐ Plan what illustrations or graphics you will put into your brochure.

STEP 3: Checklist

☐ My brochure is neat and well organized.

☐ My brochure has accurate information.

☐ My brochure has pictures or graphics that go well with the information.

☐ I checked the spelling.

☐ I checked the punctuation.

☐ My brochure is attractive.

What Does an Engineer Do?

Engineers are people who build all types of things that make our world work better. Many of the things you see and use every day were created by engineers. Some engineers work with chemicals to create new textiles, more flexible plastics, and stronger building materials. Others work in cities to build roads, bridges, and skyscrapers. Some engineers make medical supplies for hospitals and technology for space travel, and find new and safer ways to clean up the environment. Engineers can build or create just about anything!

There are many different types of engineers.

Civil engineers make structures and systems that help cities and industries work and grow. They build bridges, highways, railways, skyscrapers, engines and machines, airplanes and rocket ships.

Chemical engineers work with chemicals to find new ways of producing and improving the goods we use. They make such things as safer foods, softer and warmer clothing, new types of plastics, and textiles that do not catch fire.

Environmental engineers work to find ways of solving problems that affect animals, plants, and humans. They find ways to clean up polluted water and air, and to safely dispose of toxic wastes to make Earth cleaner and safer.

Audio engineers work with sound, and the programs and equipment that create, record, and share that sound. They create the music, audio books, and radio programs we listen to. They also create the fun and exciting sound effects and music for movies, television shows, and video games.

Computer engineers create programs to run your computer and to make it more useful and fun. They also help provide hospitals with programs that control X-ray machines and keep track of patient information.

Optical engineers make technologies that use and control light. These engineers create eyeglasses, camera lenses, televisions, telescopes, microscopes, lasers, solar cells, and broadband networks that bring the Internet into homes.

Electrical engineers work with electricity. They help build power stations. They also design the power lines that carry the electricity to where it is needed. Electricity helps your furnace to heat your home, and powers your lights, phone, computer, television, and appliances. Electricity also powers streetlights, traffic lights, and entire cities.

Can you imagine what life would be like without paved roads, radios, computers, phones, television, refrigerators, plastics, apartment buildings, or electric lights? Without the hard work of so many types of engineers, our lives would be very different!

"What Does an Engineer Do?"—Think About It!

1. What type of engineer would you like to be? Explain why.

_____

_____

_____

_____

_____

_____

2. How do engineers help people in their daily life?

_____

_____

_____

_____

_____

_____

_____

_____

Think Like an Engineer

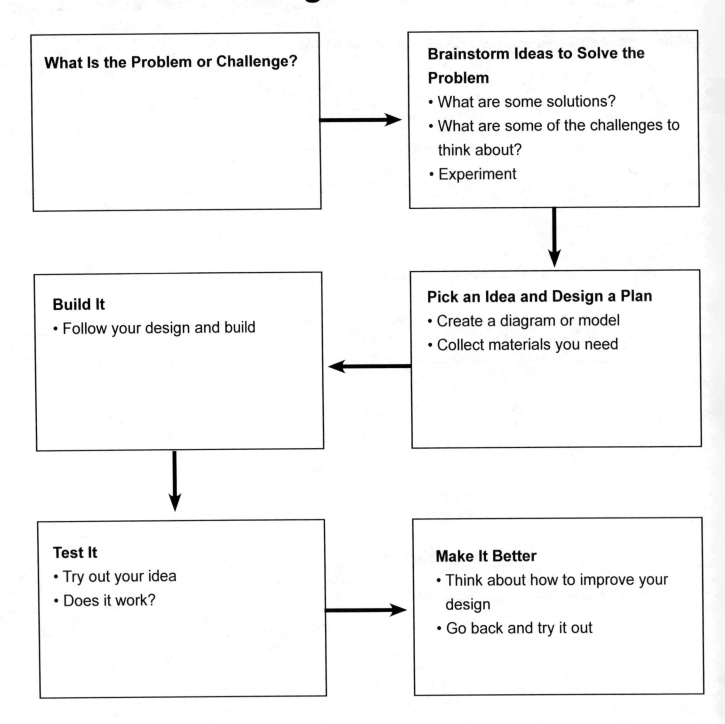

What Is the Problem or Challenge?

Brainstorm Ideas to Solve the Problem
- What are some solutions?
- What are some of the challenges to think about?
- Experiment

Build It
- Follow your design and build

Pick an Idea and Design a Plan
- Create a diagram or model
- Collect materials you need

Test It
- Try out your idea
- Does it work?

Make It Better
- Think about how to improve your design
- Go back and try it out

Remember to be patient. Take your time to figure things out.

Inventor Oral Presentation Outline

Choose an invention you are interested in. Research the inventor and how the invention was created. Think about how the invention has helped people or changed the world. Some ideas include

- a type of medicine, such as penicillin
- transportation such as a car or an airplane
- an everyday item such as the zipper or camera

Inventor: _____

Invention: _____

Introduction Checklist

I introduced my topic in an attention-grabbing way, such as by using:

- ❏ a quote
- ❏ a statistic
- ❏ an example
- ❏ a question

❏ I state what I am going to talk about in one of three sentences.

_____

_____

_____

_____

_____

_____

Body Checklist

❏ My main point has supporting details, examples, or descriptions.

❏ I wrote out my ideas the way I would sound if I were explaining, showing, or telling someone in person during a conversation.

❏ I read aloud what I wrote.

Tip: You do not have to use full sentences. Write it the same way you talk.

Main Point 1

_____

_____

_____

Supporting Details

_____

_____

_____

_____

_____

_____

_____

_____

Body Checklist

❏ My main point has supporting details, examples, or descriptions.
❏ I wrote out my ideas the way I would sound if I were explaining, showing, or telling someone in person during a conversation.
❏ I read aloud what I wrote.

Tip: You do not have to use full sentences. Write it the same way you talk.

Main Point 2

_____

_____

_____

Supporting Details

_____

_____

_____

_____

_____

_____

_____

_____

Body Checklist

❏ My main point has supporting details, examples, or descriptions.

❏ I wrote out my ideas the way I would sound if I were explaining, showing, or telling someone in person during a conversation.

❏ I read aloud what I wrote.

Tip: You do not have to use full sentences. Write it the same way you talk.

Main Point 3

_____

_____

_____

Supporting Details

_____

_____

_____

_____

_____

_____

_____

_____

Conclusion Checklist

☐ I summarized my key points.
☐ I ended my oral presentation in an attention-grabbing way, such as by using:
   ☐ a quote
   ☐ a statistic
   ☐ a question

_____

_____

_____

_____

_____

_____

_____

_____

_____

_____

Presentation Delivery Tips

• Practise! Practise! Practise! Get comfortable with what you have written.
• Highlight your good copy in places where you would like to pause for effect, or emphasize a point.
• Think about hand gestures and making eye contact with the audience or camera.
• Think about how your tone of voice can show enthusiasm, emotion, or volume.

Crazy Colouring Ideas

Have children practice their fine motor skills using different media to colour colouring pages, or simple geometric shapes.

Colour a colouring page or large geometric shapes:

- on different surfaces, such as sandpaper, to create interesting textures
- alternating heavy and light strokes
- using only primary colours
- using only secondary colours
- using different shades of the same colour
- with different colours of chalk and setting it with hairspray
- using pastels
- using watercolours
- using vertical lines
- using horizontal lines

Fill in sections of a colouring page or geometric shape using:

- different colours of modelling clay
- tiny bits of torn construction paper
- mixed media
- different colours of thick yarn
- different patterns
- cotton swab dots

Excellent drawing and painting materials:

- crayons
- pencils
- pastels
- chalk
- charcoal
- ink pen
- water-based markers
- acrylic paint
- makeup
- tempera paint
- felt tip pens
- pencil crayons
- watercolours
- food colouring

Sketchbook Drawing Ideas

Portrait

- Draw a self-portrait. Look at yourself in a mirror for reference.
- Draw a portrait of yourself 50 years from now.
- Draw a portrait of a friend or family member. Think about how you can show something about their personality in the portrait.
- Recreate a black-and-white photograph. Think about the tones in the photograph and how to imitate them.
- Practise drawing different eyes, lips, noses, ears, and types of hair. Look through magazines and other materials to find a variety of sizes, shapes, and poses.
- Draw a series of portraits of a family member using photographs taken at different stages of their life. For example, baby, child, teenager, adult, and senior. Think about what physical characteristics remain constant.
- Practise drawing different parts of the body in various positions. Ask a friend or family member to model arms, legs, heads, and shoulders.
- Draw a series of hands in a variety of positions or overlapping them.

Design

- Design a CD cover for your favourite group or singer.
- Design a magazine cover for your favourite magazine.
- Design a logo for your school or a school team.
- Design an advertisement for a vacation destination.
- Design a new cover for a book.
- Design a tattoo for a specific person.
- Design the can for a new drink.
- Design the outside of your dream house.
- Design your ultimate bedroom.
- Design a new Canadian stamp.
- Design a new Canadian coin.
- Design a new outfit.
- Design a car.
- Design a new Canadian flag.
- Design a cityscape from the future.

Still Life

- Draw an attractive flower arrangement.
- Draw a plant in great detail.
- Draw a piece of furniture with attention to colour, shading, and texture.
- Draw a stuffed animal.
- Draw a favourite toy.
- Draw a bowl of fruit.
- Draw an arrangement of three-dimensional figures with attention to shading.

How to Draw a Wolf

Follow these steps to draw. Write an adventure story about the wolf.

1

2

3

4

5

Createww a Geometric Design

Use only primary colours, or only secondary colours to colour the geometric design.

Create your own geometric design and colour it.

Cutout Art

Create a picture using images cut out of old magazines.

Symmetrical Drawings

Cut out a face or object from a magazine. Cut it in half and glue it onto the paper. Draw and colour the other half of the face using the grid as a guide.

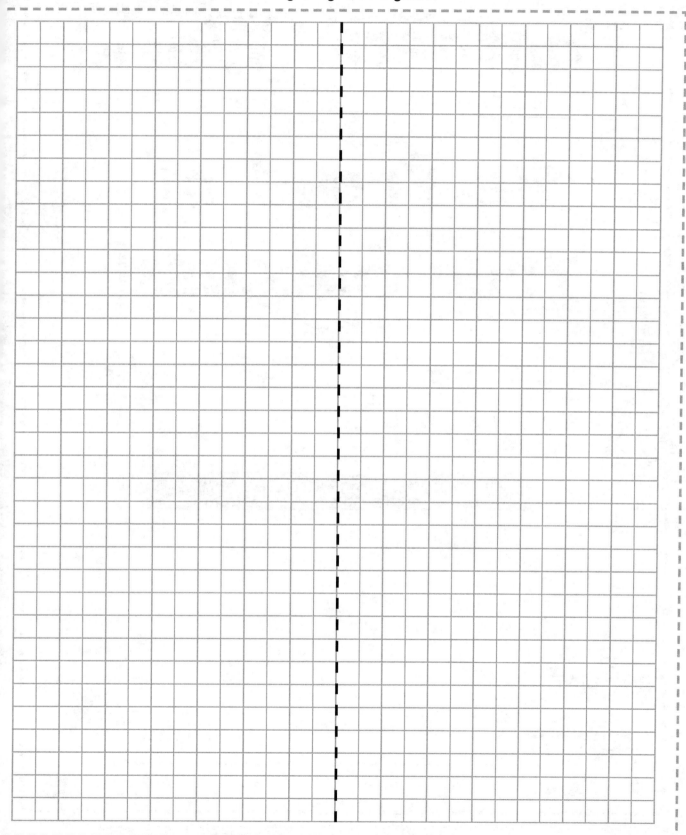

Certificate of Merit—Grade 6

Fantastic Work!

Be Proud of Your Success!

READY FOR ANYTHING!

Name

Week 1 p. 5

Mon. **1.** 32 **2.** 9 **3.** start at 2, multiply by 2 add 1 **4.** 295 **5.** 3, 6, 12

Tues. **1.** 275 **2.** 28 229, 28 989, 28 999 **3.** 12.5
4. two hundred thirty-four thousand three hundred forty **5.** $7.25

Wed. **1.** ans. can vary ▭ ▯ ▱ **2.** right **3.** ⇐ **4.** 2 **5.** acute

Thurs. **1.** 300 000 **2.** 0.0007km **3.** b **4.** 56m^2 **5.** 6.8m

Fri. **1.** 42 **2.** Panthers **3.** 49 **4.** 50 **5. bar graph**

Brain Stretch **1.** c **2.** c **3.** c **4.** p **5.** c **6.** c

Week 2 p. 8

Mon. **1.** 3, 30, 300 **2.** 111 **3.** 425 **4.** ans. will vary **5.** ◇

Tues. **1.** 9129, 9291, 19 912 **2.** eight hundred seventy-six dollars and ninety cents
3. < **4.** 1/8, 4/8, 5/8, 7/8 **5.** 81

Wed. **1.** 5 **2.** b **3.** rhombus **4.** 8 **5.** an angle more than 90° and less than 180°

Thurs. **1.** September **2.** baking a cake **3.** 5000ml **4.** 13 **5.** <

Fri. **1.** 20 **2.** 36 **3.** 129, 142 **4.** Cameron, 162 cm

Brain Stretch $90

Week 3 p. 11

Mon. **1.** 10 **2.** 101 **3.** 55, 44 **4.** 3, 15, 75 **5.** 3

Tues. **1.** $1.29 **2.** 6/10 or 3/5 **3.** 342 **4.** 1110 1101, 1011, 1001, **5.** 1300

Wed. **1.** trapezoid **2.** 1 **3.** congruent **4.** 4 **5.** an angle less than 90°

Thurs. **1.** 10 months **2.** 69m **3.** 4cm^2 **4.** 730 **5.** b

Fri. **1.** comedy **2.** drama **3.** 10 **4.** 70 **5.** ans. will vary

Brain Stretch **1.** thousands **2.** tens **3.** ten thousands **4.** ones **5.** ten thousands **6.** hundred thousands

Week 4 p. 14

Mon. **1.** 488, 484, 480 **2.** 30, 38, 46 **3.** start at 3, multiply by 4 **4.** 14 **5.** 9/24

Tues. **1.** 5600 **2.** 1, 2, 7, 14 **3.** 1127 **4.** $10 bill, 2 x toonies, 3 x quarters, 2 x dimes, 3 x pennies **5.** =

Wed. **1.** c **2.** a **3.** rectangular prism **4.** parallelogram/ rhombus **5.** 4 sided polygon

Thurs. **1.** 0.89cl **2.** 11:04pm **3.** garbage can **4.** 34 **5.** >

Fri. **1.** 6 **2.** 1, 2, 3, 4, 5, 6 **3.** 1/2 **4.** 1/2 **5.** 1/6

Brain Stretch 8 squares

Week 5 p. 17

Mon. **1.** ans. will vary **2.** 3 **3.** start at 37, subtract 4 **4.** 22, 27 **5.** c

Tues. **1.** 3/4 **2.** 702, 782, 827, 872 **3.** a **4.** 9471 **5.** seventy-seven dollars and thirty-five cents

Wed. **1.** cylinder **2.** circle **3.** 3 **4.** b **5.** 5

Thurs. **1.** a **2.** 9.6mm **3.** 312 weeks **4.** a **5.** 12 000

Fri. ans. will vary **1.** likely **2.** likely **3.** certain **4.** likely **5.** likely **6.** certain

Brain Stretch **1.** 2385 **2.** 4536 **3.** 19.52 **4.** 8.14 **5.** 71.40

Week 6   p. 20

Mon.   **1.** 88   **2.** ans. will vary   **3.** 96, 192   **4.** 2   **5.** start at 50, subtract 1, then subtract one more each time

Tues.   **1.** 1, 2, 4, 5, 8, 10, 20, 40   **2.** 1xfifty, 2xdimes, 3xpennies   **3.** 2/9, 5/9, 7/9   **4.** 6.931   **5.** eight thousand nine hundred fifty-four

Wed.   **1.** 1   **2.** yes   **3.** cube   **4.** acute   **5.** 8

Thurs.   **1.** a   **2.** 1988   **3.** 26m   **4.** 220mm   **5.** b

Fri.   **1.** b   **2.** f   **3.** i   **4.** d   **5.** j   **6.** h   **7.** c   **8.** a   **9.** e   **10.** g

Brain Stretch   **1.** 100 000 + 30 000 + 2000 + 500 + 40 + 7   **2.** 30 000 + 3000 + 600 + 50+ 1
3. 90 000 + 4000 + 800 + 30   **4.** 100 000 + 90 000 + 1000+200 + 30 + 4

Week 7   p. 23

Mon.   **1.** 127   **2.** start at 1, add 10   **3.** 947   **4.** 72, 80, 88   **5.** 354

Tues.   **1.** 655 012   **2.** 1233   **3.** 1980   **4.** 564   **5.** 2 pieces

Wed.   **1.** sphere   **2.** 5   **3.** a   **4.** 4   **5.** b

Thurs.   **1.** 7:30, 10.5hrs per week   **2.** 63m   **3.** 10521.067g   **4.** 3720   **5.** 6.82 kg

Fri.   **1.** 310   **2.** 190   **3.** 120   **4.** bar graph   **5.** 6

Brain Stretch   **1.** 156 hours   **2.** 1560 hours

Week 8   p. 26

Mon.   **1.** 60   **2.** b   **3.** 112   **4.** 23, 36, 62   **5.** start at 500, divide by 10

Tues.   **1.** $776.51   **2.** hundreds   **3.** 5.7   **4.** 400 000 + 80 000 + 2 000 + 900 + 30 + 7   **5.** 18

Wed.   **1.** cone   **2.** a   **3.** an angle greater than 90° and less than 180°   **4.** 40 degrees   **5.** 0

Thurs.   **1.** 56m   **2.** a   **3.** 0.559m   **4.** kg   **5.** 256 mins

Fri.   **1.** approx. 16   **2.** 21/100 or 18.9/90   **3.** 52/100 or 46.8/90   **4.** 39%   **5.** Bus

Brain Stretch   **1.** 400km   **2.** 800km

Week 9   p. 29

Mon.   **1.** 145, 289, 577   **2.** start at 1, x5-1   **3.** 454, 444, 434   **4.** 27   **5.** growing

Tues.   **1.** >   **2.** $80.88   **3.** one hundred twenty-eight thousand four hundred   **4.** c   **5.** 56

Wed.   **1.** 4 sided polygon   **2.** 60^0 **3.**   **4.** rectangular prism   **5.** c

Thurs.   **1.** 84   **2.** 370ml   **3.** 28m^2 **4.** 0.37km   **5.** m

Fri.   **1.** 148   **2.** Kaitlyn   **3.** Madelyn and Michael/ Spencer and Megan   **4.** 48   **5.** 8

Brain Stretch 2 is the better buy because each book is $9

Week 10   p. 32

Mon.   **1.** start at 78, add 7 to the column to the left   **2.** 62   **3.** 30 000 000   **4.** 20, 43, 89   **5.** 111

Tues.   **1.** 70 + 7 + 0.01   **2.** 7.996   **3.** 3/4   **4.** 149 141   **5.** 17/5

Wed.   **1.** (☺)   **2.** 1   **3.** 120^0 **4.** 2   **5.** 6

Thurs.   **1.** mm or cm   **2.** 9m x 9m   **3.** 1000 years   **4.** 3:20:15   **5.** 18 m

Fri.   **1.** approx. 7   **2.** ¼ or 25/100   **3.** 45/100 or 36/80   **4.** 30%   **5.** summer

Brain Stretch   **1.** 0.227   **2.** 0.014   **3.** 8.65   **4.** 3.71   **5.** 5.722   **6.** 8.412

Week 11   p. 35

Mon. **1.** 12 **2.** 10, 15, 30 **3.** b **4.** shrinking **5.** 45, 36, 27

Tues. **1.** 41.279 **2.** 5 3/4 **3.** 45 789.6 **4.** b **5.** 25 330

Wed. **1.** triangle **2.** acute **3.** 1 **4.** 180^0 **5.** 1 or 0 – ans. may vary - discuss

Thurs. **1.** 299mm **2.** $18.9m^2$ **3.** kg **4.** 4 **5.** 9cm

Fri. **1.** 93 **2.** 15 **3.** 13 **4.** 16.8 or rounded to 17

Brain Stretch 1. 25/30 or 5/6   2. 16.6%

Week 12   p. 38

Mon. **1.** 0.009 **2.** 100 **3.** 190, 175, 160 **4.** a **5.** 200km

Tues. **1.** 240 **2.** 5/6 **3.** 98 521 **4.** 0.3 **5.** 100

Wed. **1.** 60^0 **2.** a **3.** c **4.** 0 **5.** 8

Thurs. **1.** 12:57 pm **2.** 40 **3.** 38 **4.** 24 cm^2 **5.** 73 100

Fri. 1. 16.2, 9, 18, 20 **2.** 13, 16, 16.5, 17 **3.** 20.6, 5, 21, 21 **4.** 4, 3, 5, 5 **5.** 13, 15, 10, 10

Brain Stretch   154

Week 13   p. 41

Mon. **1.** square **2.** repeating **3.** 1422 **4.** 10, 20, 40 **5.** 10

Tues. **1.** 9/100 **2.** 0.54 **3.** 276.0 **4.** 79.375 **5.** 375

Wed. **1.** isosceles **2.** 0 **3.** 24cm^3 **4.** 8 **5.** slide

Thurs. **1.** 185 cm **2.** 3cm **3.** 44cm **4.** 3pm **5.** 60

Fri. **1.** 90 **2.** football, basketball, baseball, hockey **3.** 55 **4.** hockey **5.** football

Brain Stretch   193 boxes

Week 14   p. 44

Mon. **1.** 22 **2.** 3 **3.** 55 **4.** start at 5, add 3 **5.** 90, 86, 82

Tues. **1.** 42 **2.** 0.01, 0.11, 1.01, 1.10 **3.** 87 481 **4.** 123 904 **5.** 12

Wed. **1.** right **2.** 0 **3.** cube **4.** 60 m^2 **5.** 4

Thurs. **1.** 6000 **2.** 8:00pm **3.** $280m^2$ **4.** 4:30 **5.** 25cm

Fri. factors for 45: 1, 3, 5, 9, 15, 45 factors for 36: 1, 2, 3, 4, 6, 9, 12, 18, 36 both: 1,3, 9,

Brain Stretch **1.** $2.40 **2.** 2

Week 15   p. 47

Mon. **1.** 8 **2.** 8, 16, 24, 32, 40 **3.** start at 30, add 30 **4.** 384 **5.** face

Tues. **1.** 101.23 **2.** a **3.** 24 **4.** 20 **5.** 216

Wed. **1.** sphere **2.** 2 **3.** c **4.** 60^0 **5.** parallel

Thurs. **1.** km **2.** 36 000 **3.** 1/2bxh **4.** 8cm **5.** 225km

Fri. **1.** 18 **2.** 10 **3.** chocolate **4.** bubble gum

Brain Stretch $67.50, No, because that is not enough.

Week 16   p. 50

Mon.   **1.** 411, 415, 419 **2.** 12 **3.** ⬇ **4.** 120 legs **5.** 5

Tues.   **1.** 11, 13, 17, 19 **2.** 490.119 **3.** 0.0012 **4.** 202 **5.** -11, -10, -6, 9, 14, 15

Wed.   **1.** both are quadrilaterals, have parallel lines & right angles **2.** 4 **3.** 1 pair **4.** right **5.** 30^0

Thurs.   **1.** 4 **2.** ml **3.** 20:00 **4.** 10:33 am **5.** 72m

Fri.   **1.** blue **2.** orange, red, purple **3.** blue **4.** orange, red, purple

Brain Stretch $9.65

Week 17   p. 53

Mon.   **1.** 19.7 **2.** 5.1, 5.22, 5.5, 5.6 **3.** 2.5116 **4.** 15, 16, 17, 18, 19 **5.** 844

Tues.   **1.** 60 **2.** 879 **3.** $2574 **4.** 12459 **5.** b

Wed.   **1.** 5 **2.** a **3.** an angle greater than 90° **4.** 180^0 **5.** b

Thurs.   **1.** 6 hours **2.** 24cm **3.** ml or L **4.** $404m^2$ **5.** $3215.36m^2$

Fri.   **1.** June, July and August **2.** July **3.** 250mm

Brain Stretch   Case of 24 is the best buy

Week 18   p. 56

Mon.   **1.** start at 10, x2+3 **2.** growing **3.** 31 **4.** 36 **5.** 16

Tues.   **1.** $2.50 **2.** 4, 9, 15 **3.** 50% **4.** 10.19 **5.** 56 410

Wed.   **1.** straight **2.** no **3.** b **4.** 20^0 **5.** congruent

Thurs.   **1.** both lxw or lxh, same **2.** 56 **3.** 156 **4.** 17:30 **5.** $803.84m^2$

Fri.   **1.** Factors for 72: 1, 2, 3, 4, 6, 8, 9, 12, 18, 24, 36, 72 Factors for 48: 1, 2, 3, 4, 6, 8, 12, 16, 24, 48
        Both: 1, 2, 3, 4, 6, 8, 12, 24

Brain Stretch   0.84kg

Week 19   p. 59

Mon.   **1.** 21, 22, 23, 24, 25 **2.** 880, 855, 830 **3.** 21 **4.** 54 **5.** 45

Tues.   **1.** -30, -24, 17, 47 **2.** 25/7 **3.** 31.2 **4.** 18:12 **5.** $44.95

Wed.   **1.** turn **2.** 1 **3.** similar **4.** c **5.** a

Thurs.   **1.** 32cm **2.** 60 **3.** $192cm^2$ **4.** 4600dm **5.** 100km

Fri.   A. 162 B. 24

Brain Stretch   Paul

Week 20   p. 62

Mon.   **1.** 29 **2.** 4, 6, 8, 10, 12 **3.** 36 **4.** ans will vary **5.** 2700

Tues.   **1.** a **2.** c **3.** $7.05 **4.** 13.53 **5.** 918 055

Wed.   **1.** 12 **2.** congruent **3.** acute angle **4.** isosceles **5.** 12

Thurs.   **1.** a **2.** 2:24 pm **3.** 1989 **4.** 500 000mm **5.** 7.25 hours

Fri.   **1.** mean=340 **2.** mean=136

Brain Stretch 125.6 cm

Week 21 p. 65

Mon. **1.** 25 **2.** 22 **3.** 35, 34, 33, 32, 31 **4.** 7 **5.** 12

Tues. **1.** 270 **2.** 12.1 **3.** forty-nine thousand one hundred fifty-six **4.** 1008 **5.** 74109

Wed. **1.** a **2.** 2 intersecting **3.** 0 **4.** d. none **5.** rectangular prism

Thurs. **1.** 4:09 **2.** thermometer **3.** 12 **4.** 48m^3 **5.** 65cm

Fri. **1.** Wednesday **2.** Monday, Friday **3.** 190 cars **4.** Wednesday **5.** 20

Brain Stretch 14

Week 22 p. 68

Mon. **1.** 111.15 **2.** 169 **3.** 0.001 **4.** white heart **5.** ans will vary

Tues. **1.** c **2.** 2000 **3.** 40 **4.** < **5.** 10

Wed. **1.** 0 **2.** quadrilaterals **3.** 12 **4.** obtuse **5.** rectangle or square

Thurs. **1.** 12000dm **2.** 7:35 **3.** a **4.** 1939 **5.** a

Fri. **1.** 6 **2.** 11 cm **3.** 6 **4.** 13 **5.** 2cm

Brain Stretch 7

Week 23 p. 71

Mon. **1.** 414 **2.** 23 **3.** b **4.** 14 **5.** ans will vary

Tues. **1.** 54,60,66 **2.** 4 **3.** 500 000+60 000+9000+800+30+1 **4.** a **5.** 0.8

Wed. **1.** 15^0 **2.** ans. will vary (sphere, cylinder, cone) **3.** see flip **4.** hexagon, rectangle or square
 5. rectangular prism

Thurs. **1.** b **2.** 28cm **3.** 0.178 **4.** 7:08 **5.** 126 m^2

Fri. **1.** 19:58 **2.** 13:58 **3.** 8:32 **4.** 18:8

Brain Stretch 125

Week 24 p. 74

Mon. **1.** 175 **2.** 20 **3.** a **4.** 9 **5.** ans will vary

Tues. **1.** 4 **2.** eight hundred two thousand three hundred **3.** 745.13 **4.** 31 **5.** 8/100, 2/25

Wed. **1.** same size and shape **2.** same shape **3.** cube **4.** 0 **5.** b

Thurs. **1.** 14 hours 30 minutes **2.** 5 000 000cm **3.** 288m^2 **4.** 56 **5.** 3.6 m^2

Fri. **1.** class b **2.** $44 **3.** week 3 **4.** $52

Brain Stretch 1005 people

Week 25 p. 77

Mon. **1.** b **2.** ans will vary **3.** 744 **4.** 5, 11, 17, 23, 29 **5.** 7

Tues. **1.** 17 1/2 **2.** 1350 **3.** $422.19 **4.** 44 053 **5.** 8

Wed. **1.** see drawing **2.** 1 **3.** 360^0 **4.** b **5.** a

Thurs. **1.** 720 **2.** 52mm^2 **3.** 650 000cm **4.** 100 **5.** 26km/hr

Fri. **1.** 10 **2.** 10 **3.** 10 **4.** 188 **5.** yes

Brain Stretch b is $8 each

Test 1—Multiplying by 1 to 6

```
  7    4   12    8    4    6    9
 ×2   ×4   ×6   ×5   ×1   ×3   ×2
 14   16   72   40    4   18   18

 12    8   11    6    4    7   10
 ×5   ×3   ×2   ×5   ×6   ×4   ×2
 60   24   22   30   24   28   20

  7   12    3    1    4    6
 ×6   ×3   ×2   ×3   ×5   ×6
 42   36    6    3   20   36
```
Number Correct ___/20

Test 2—Multiplying by 1 to 6

```
  6    7   12    4    5    9    4
 ×4   ×3   ×5   ×3   ×5   ×2   ×1
 24   21   60   12   25   18    4

  2   11   10    8    7    9    4
 ×6   ×2   ×3   ×6   ×1   ×4   ×4
 12   22   30   48    7   36   16

  8    5    3    1   10   11
 ×3   ×2   ×5   ×1   ×4   ×6
 24   10   15    1   40   66
```
Number Correct ___/20

95

Test 3—Multiplying by 1 to 6

```
 11    8    9    3    1    5   12
 ×3   ×1   ×5   ×4   ×2   ×5   ×4
 33    8   45   12    2   25   48

  7    4    2   11    3    8    6
 ×6   ×5   ×1   ×6   ×2   ×5   ×2
 42   20    2   66    6   40   12

  6   10    8    9    5    6
 ×4   ×2   ×3   ×6   ×3   ×3
 24   20   24   54   15   18
```
Number Correct ___/20

Test 4—Multiplying by 1 to 6

```
  5    9   11    8    7   10    8
 ×4   ×1   ×3   ×4   ×3   ×5   ×6
 20    9   33   32   21   50   48

  3   11    2   10    6    6    5
 ×3   ×4   ×1   ×6   ×5   ×3   ×6
  9   44    2   60   30   18   30

  3    7   12    9    9   10
 ×1   ×2   ×5   ×6   ×2   ×4
  3   14   60   54   18   40
```
Number Correct ___/20

96

Test 5—Multiplying by 1 to 6

```
  7   10    1    4   12    4    3
 ×2   ×6   ×2   ×5   ×3   ×4   ×4
 14   60    2   20   36   16   12

  9    6    3   11   10    7    5
 ×5   ×4   ×5   ×2   ×3   ×6   ×6
 45   24   15   22   30   42   30

 12   11    2    6    8    9
 ×6   ×1   ×5   ×3   ×1   ×2
 72   11   10   18    8   18
```
Number Correct ___/20

Test 6—Multiplying by 1 to 6

```
  5    3    8    8   12    1    9
 ×4   ×3   ×3   ×6   ×1   ×2   ×6
 20    9   24   48   12    2   54

  9    4    3    5    3    8    6
 ×4   ×1   ×2   ×3   ×4   ×4   ×6
 36    4    6   15   12   32   36

 10    6   12   11    5    2
 ×4   ×5   ×6   ×5   ×1   ×5
 40   30   72   55    5   10
```
Number Correct ___/20

97

Test 7—Multiplying by 1 to 6

```
  7    5    7    5   10    6    6
 ×3   ×2   ×6   ×6   ×5   ×4   ×2
 21   10   42   30   50   24   12

  8   12    2   11    1    1    9
 ×5   ×4   ×5   ×3   ×3   ×1   ×2
 40   48   10   33    3    1   18

  6    8    2   12    4   10
 ×5   ×4   ×1   ×6   ×3   ×1
 30   32    2   72   12   10
```
Number Correct ___/20

Test 8—Multiplying by 1 to 6

```
 11    5    5    1   12   10    4
 ×4   ×3   ×2   ×6   ×5   ×4   ×3
 44   15   10    6   60   40   12

  9    4    6    4    3    3    8
 ×3   ×6   ×5   ×2   ×3   ×1   ×4
 27   24   30    8    9    3   32

  3   10   11    8    7    3
 ×4   ×2   ×6   ×5   ×3   ×2
 12   20   66   40   21    6
```
Number Correct ___/20

98

Test 9—Multiplying by 1 to 6

```
  3   11    5    9    3    7    4
 ×6   ×2   ×1   ×5   ×2   ×6   ×3
 18   22    5   45    6   42   12

  2   11    8    9    6    9    6
 ×4   ×3   ×6   ×2   ×4   ×4   ×6
  8   33   48   18   24   36   36

  7    7    8   10   12    8
 ×5   ×4   ×2   ×5   ×2   ×3
 35   28   16   50   24   24
```
Number Correct ___/20

Test 10—Multiplying by 1 to 6

```
  7    6    8    5    1   10    9
 ×2   ×6   ×3   ×2   ×4   ×2   ×6
 14   36   24   10    4   20   54

  9   10   12   11    2    7    6
 ×4   ×1   ×3   ×5   ×6   ×1   ×2
 36   10   36   55   12    7   12

  3    4    4    7    2    5
 ×4   ×5   ×3   ×4   ×2   ×5
 12   20   12   28    4   25
```
Number Correct ___/20

99

Test 1—Multiplying by 7 to 12

```
 11    8    8    9   10    3    4
 ×7  ×10  ×12   ×9  ×11   ×7  ×12
 77   80   96   81  110   21   48

 11    3    7    6    4    7    9
×11   ×8   ×7  ×12  ×10  ×12   ×8
121   24   49   72   40   84   72

  2    6    8    9   12    9
 ×8  ×11   ×9   ×7  ×10  ×11
 16   66   72   63  120   99
```
Number Correct ___/20

Test 2—Multiplying by 7 to 12

```
  7   12    5    7    4    8    9
×10   ×9  ×11   ×7   ×8  ×12   ×7
 70  108   55   49   32   96   63

 12   10    3   10    8    6    4
 ×8  ×10   ×8  ×12   ×7   ×9  ×11
 96  100   24  120   56   54   44

  6   10   11    9    2    8
×12   ×8   ×7  ×11  ×10   ×9
 72   80   77   99   20   72
```
Number Correct ___/20

100

Test 3—Multiplying by 7 to 12

```
  9    3    5   11   10    9    3
×11  ×10  ×10   ×8  ×12   ×9   ×7
 99   30   50   88  120   81   21

 11   10    6    6    7    8   12
×11   ×7  ×12   ×8   ×7   ×8   ×9
121   70   72   48   49   64  108

 12    9    8    6    2    2
×10  ×12  ×11   ×7   ×9  ×11
120  108   88   42   18   22
```
Number Correct ___/20

Test 4—Multiplying by 7 to 12

```
  7    5    9    4   11   12    2
×12   ×8  ×10   ×9   ×7  ×11   ×8
 84   40   90   36   77  132   16

  3   10    5    8    4    2    1
×10   ×8  ×12   ×9  ×10   ×7  ×10
 30   80   60   72   40   14   10

  9    1    3    7    6    6
 ×8  ×12  ×11  ×10   ×9   ×8
 72   12   33   70   54   48
```
Number Correct ___/20

101

Test 5—Multiplying by 7 to 12

```
  2   12    8    9   11    6    7
×11  ×10   ×9  ×10   ×8  ×12   ×7
 22  120   72   90   88   72   49

  9    5    6    4    7   10    7
 ×8   ×9  ×10   ×7   ×8   ×7  ×11
 72   45   60   28   56   70   77

  8    3    7   12   10   10
×11  ×12   ×9   ×7  ×12  ×10
 88   36   63   84  120  100
```
Number Correct ___/20

Test 6—Multiplying by 7 to 12

```
 10    4    5    1    7   12    9
 ×7  ×10   ×8  ×12  ×11   ×7   ×8
 70   40   40   12   77   84   72

  5    8   12    3   11    3    7
×11  ×10   ×9   ×8  ×10  ×12   ×9
 55   80  108   24  110   36   63

  9    6    8    4    9    6
×11  ×12   ×8   ×9   ×7   ×7
 99   72   64   36   63   42
```
Number Correct ___/20

102

Test 7—Multiplying by 7 to 12

```
 11    7    7   10    1    6    4
 ×9   ×8   ×7  ×10   ×8   ×9  ×11
 99   56   49  100    8   54   44

  6   12    5    9    3   12    9
 ×8   ×9  ×12  ×10   ×8  ×10   ×7
 48  108   60   90   24  120   63

  6    8    8    5    9    8
 ×7   ×9  ×12   ×7  ×11  ×10
 42   72   96   35   99   80
```
Number Correct ___/20

Test 8—Multiplying by 7 to 12

```
  8    8    9    3    4   11    6
×12   ×8   ×9  ×11  ×10   ×7   ×8
 96   64   81   33   40   77   48

  7    8   10    6    1    6    4
 ×7  ×10   ×9  ×11   ×7  ×12   ×9
 49   80   90   66    7   72   36

  7    6   12   10    3    7
×10  ×12   ×7  ×11   ×8   ×9
 70   60   84  110   24   63
```
Number Correct ___/20

103

Test 9—Multiplying by 7 to 12

9 ×10 = 90	7 ×12 = 84	4 ×9 = 36	8 ×8 = 64	8 ×11 = 88	10 ×10 = 100	12 ×7 = 84
1 ×10 = 10	3 ×11 = 33	6 ×8 = 48	4 ×12 = 48	5 ×7 = 35	2 ×8 = 16	9 ×9 = 81
6 ×11 = 66	2 ×7 = 14	7 ×8 = 56	11 ×12 = 132	4 ×10 = 40	10 ×9 = 90	Number Correct /20

Test 10—Multiplying by 7 to 12

9 ×10 = 90	9 ×9 = 81	11 ×8 = 88	9 ×11 = 99	8 ×10 = 80	10 ×7 = 70	2 ×9 = 18
3 ×9 = 27	7 ×8 = 56	2 ×7 = 14	8 ×9 = 72	1 ×10 = 90	10 ×11 = 110	7 ×7 = 49
3 ×7 = 21	2 ×10 = 20	6 ×12 = 72	5 ×9 = 45	11 ×7 = 77	12 ×11 = 132	Number Correct /20

`04`

Test 1—Multiplying by 1 to 12

3 ×7 = 21	4 ×6 = 24	8 ×11 = 88	11 ×3 = 33	10 ×2 = 20	4 ×4 = 16	6 ×5 = 30
7 ×5 = 35	9 ×10 = 90	12 ×6 = 72	2 ×4 = 8	7 ×8 = 56	5 ×1 = 5	8 ×5 = 40
11 ×6 = 66	8 ×2 = 16	10 ×7 = 70	2 ×5 = 10	12 ×12 = 144	9 ×9 = 81	Number Correct /20

Test 2—Multiplying by 1 to 12

5 ×2 = 10	7 ×6 = 42	4 ×9 = 36	4 ×12 = 48	6 ×6 = 36	2 ×2 = 4	3 ×8 = 24
12 ×1 = 12	11 ×10 = 110	9 ×8 = 72	6 ×2 = 12	10 ×10 = 100	7 ×3 = 21	8 ×5 = 40
3 ×11 = 33	6 ×7 = 42	3 ×4 = 12	1 ×5 = 5	9 ×4 = 36	8 ×7 = 56	Number Correct /20

`105`

Test 3—Multiplying by 1 to 12

11 ×5 = 55	4 ×9 = 36	9 ×2 = 18	7 ×3 = 21	4 ×2 = 8	10 ×1 = 10	2 ×8 = 16
10 ×6 = 60	8 ×10 = 80	5 ×5 = 25	8 ×4 = 32	8 ×7 = 56	7 ×5 = 35	10 ×8 = 80
4 ×1 = 4	9 ×12 = 108	11 ×11 = 121	6 ×9 = 54	6 ×8 = 48	9 ×3 = 27	Number Correct /20

Test 4—Multiplying by 1 to 12

11 ×7 = 77	2 ×5 = 10	3 ×2 = 6	6 ×5 = 30	3 ×6 = 18	8 ×5 = 40	5 ×4 = 20
4 ×4 = 16	10 ×7 = 70	6 ×8 = 48	2 ×7 = 14	8 ×1 = 8	9 ×6 = 54	12 ×3 = 36
5 ×12 = 60	3 ×7 = 21	7 ×11 = 77	7 ×9 = 63	7 ×2 = 14	10 ×8 = 80	Number Correct /20

`106`

Test 5—Multiplying by 1 to 12

11 ×9 = 99	2 ×12 = 24	6 ×11 = 66	3 ×5 = 15	7 ×9 = 63	6 ×10 = 60	7 ×1 = 7
3 ×4 = 12	10 ×9 = 90	6 ×4 = 24	8 ×6 = 48	5 ×9 = 45	3 ×3 = 9	7 ×3 = 21
8 ×5 = 40	9 ×8 = 72	9 ×9 = 81	5 ×7 = 35	1 ×2 = 2	10 ×8 = 80	Number Correct /20

Test 6—Multiplying by 1 to 12

2 ×12 = 24	8 ×11 = 88	3 ×6 = 18	9 ×9 = 81	10 ×2 = 20	3 ×8 = 24	10 ×3 = 30
5 ×9 = 45	7 ×6 = 42	3 ×9 = 27	5 ×10 = 50	9 ×7 = 63	12 ×3 = 36	11 ×7 = 77
1 ×12 = 12	10 ×4 = 40	7 ×5 = 35	6 ×8 = 48	5 ×1 = 5	4 ×8 = 32	Number Correct /20

`07`

Test 7—Multiplying by 1 to 12

2 ×7 = 14	12 ×2 = 24	5 ×6 = 30	11 ×8 = 88	10 ×5 = 50	9 ×6 = 54	4 ×1 = 4
3 ×11 = 33	5 ×12 = 60	9 ×3 = 27	9 ×8 = 72	6 ×7 = 42	10 ×4 = 40	6 ×3 = 18
4 ×10 = 40	1 ×9 = 9	5 ×9 = 45	2 ×9 = 18	9 ×7 = 63	11 ×9 = 99	Number Correct /20

Test 8—Multiplying by 1 to 12

7 ×7 = 49	9 ×6 = 54	12 ×9 = 108	7 ×4 = 28	8 ×2 = 16	7 ×9 = 63	9 ×8 = 72
7 ×12 = 84	2 ×9 = 18	7 ×10 = 70	9 ×9 = 81	8 ×8 = 64	8 ×3 = 24	12 ×8 = 96
7 ×8 = 56	8 ×5 = 40	7 ×11 = 77	4 ×1 = 4	3 ×9 = 27	5 ×7 = 35	Number Correct /20

`108`

Test 9—Multiplying by 1 to 12

7 ×8 = 56	12 ×4 = 48	2 ×10 = 20	11 ×5 = 55	3 ×2 = 6	12 ×3 = 36	9 ×9 = 81
10 ×9 = 90	1 ×7 = 7	10 ×12 = 120	4 ×9 = 36	11 ×6 = 66	9 ×8 = 72	2 ×7 = 14
9 ×5 = 45	8 ×11 = 88	8 ×8 = 64	2 ×1 = 2	12 ×9 = 108	5 ×9 = 45	Number Correct /20

Test 10—Multiplying by 1 to 12

6 ×4 = 24	11 ×1 = 11	10 ×3 = 30	5 ×9 = 45	2 ×5 = 10	4 ×7 = 28	9 ×12 = 108
11 ×9 = 99	4 ×11 = 44	9 ×8 = 72	10 ×4 = 40	6 ×9 = 54	3 ×3 = 9	12 ×2 = 24
4 ×8 = 32	5 ×5 = 25	7 ×7 = 49	10 ×6 = 60	1 ×10 = 10	8 ×11 = 88	Number Correct /20

`109`

Test 1—Dividing by 1 to 6

35÷5 = 7	36÷3 = 12	25÷5 = 5	16÷2 = 8	12÷6 = 2	24÷6 = 4	40÷4 = 10
27÷3 = 9	3÷1 = 3	16÷4 = 4	8÷1 = 8	18÷6 = 3	55÷5 = 11	28÷4 = 7
44÷4 = 11	20÷2 = 10	10÷2 = 5	72÷6 = 12	2÷2 = 1	50÷5 = 10	Number Correct /20

Test 2—Dividing by 1 to 6

20÷2 = 10	21÷3 = 7	44÷4 = 11	18÷2 = 9	15÷3 = 5	22÷2 = 11	12÷3 = 4
45÷5 = 9	2÷1 = 2	6÷3 = 2	32÷4 = 8	8÷2 = 4	60÷5 = 12	36÷6 = 6
36÷3 = 12	35÷5 = 7	24÷3 = 8	24÷6 = 4	66÷6 = 11	30÷3 = 10	Number Correct /20

`112`

Test 3—Dividing by 1 to 6

16÷2 = 8	48÷4 = 12	8÷2 = 4	27÷3 = 9	25÷5 = 5	24÷3 = 8	72÷6 = 12
30÷6 = 5	4÷2 = 2	55÷5 = 11	36÷6 = 6	20÷2 = 10	32÷4 = 8	45÷5 = 9
35÷5 = 7	40÷4 = 10	15÷5 = 3	7÷1 = 7	9÷1 = 9	12÷2 = 6	Number Correct /20

Test 4—Dividing by 1 to 6

48÷4 = 12	11÷1 = 11	15÷3 = 5	28÷4 = 7	20÷5 = 4	4÷2 = 2	9÷1 = 9
36÷4 = 9	30÷5 = 6	40÷5 = 8	6÷2 = 3	44÷4 = 11	36÷3 = 12	60÷6 = 10
30÷3 = 10	27÷3 = 9	25÷5 = 5	36÷6 = 6	18÷6 = 3	16÷2 = 8	Number Correct /20

`113`

Test 5—Dividing by 1 to 6

36÷6 = 6	6÷2 = 3	7÷1 = 7	33÷3 = 11	3÷3 = 1	10÷5 = 2	25÷5 = 5
24÷4 = 6	15÷3 = 5	14÷2 = 7	8÷2 = 4	30÷6 = 5	44÷4 = 11	12÷3 = 4
72÷6 = 12	20÷2 = 10	32÷4 = 8	27÷3 = 9	12÷1 = 12	45÷5 = 9	Number Correct /20

Test 6—Dividing by 1 to 6

60÷5 = 12	15÷5 = 3	2÷1 = 2	36÷4 = 9	12÷6 = 2	50÷5 = 10	18÷6 = 3
12÷2 = 6	11÷1 = 11	33÷3 = 11	36÷3 = 12	14÷2 = 7	40÷4 = 10	35÷5 = 7
10÷2 = 5	32÷4 = 8	9÷1 = 9	24÷6 = 4	18÷2 = 9	4÷2 = 2	Number Correct /20

`114`

350

Test 7—Dividing by 1 to 6

10 / 2)20   7 / 2)14   6 / 5)30   7 / 3)21   9 / 4)36   5 / 2)10   11 / 6)66
6 / 6)36   12 / 2)24   5 / 6)30   4 / 3)12   12 / 4)48   10 / 5)50   9 / 5)45
3 / 3)9   5 / 3)15   4 / 5)20   11 / 4)44   8 / 3)24   10 / 1)10   Number Correct /20

Test 8—Dividing by 1 to 6

8 / 4)32   3 / 3)9   6 / 3)18   8 / 6)48   12 / 5)60   10 / 5)50   1 / 1)1
3 / 2)6   4 / 4)16   10 / 6)60   9 / 3)27   5 / 3)15   11 / 4)44   10 / 2)20
9 / 5)45   3 / 4)12   6 / 2)12   12 / 6)72   7 / 3)21   6 / 5)30   Number Correct /20

115

Test 9—Dividing by 1 to 6

11 / 2)22   9 / 1)9   12 / 6)72   8 / 4)32   11 / 6)66   2 / 5)10   6 / 3)18
3 / 1)3   7 / 5)35   10 / 2)20   4 / 6)24   7 / 3)21   11 / 4)44   3 / 5)15
10 / 4)40   12 / 2)24   3 / 3)9   8 / 2)16   6 / 2)12   5 / 5)25   Number Correct /20

Test 10—Dividing by 1 to 6

7 / 2)14   8 / 4)32   2 / 3)6   4 / 4)16   5 / 6)30   10 / 5)50   9 / 3)27
10 / 2)20   3 / 6)18   2 / 1)2   11 / 5)55   3 / 9)4   12 / 4)48   2 / 6)12
1 / 4)4   7 / 5)35   8 / 3)24   9 / 1)9   2 / 2)4   6 / 3)18   Number Correct /20

116

Test 1—Dividing by 7 to 12

1 / 10)10   2 / 12)24   9 / 9)81   11 / 8)88   6 / 11)66   8 / 8)64   12 / 7)84
6 / 7)42   11 / 7)77   4 / 9)36   5 / 11)55   9 / 8)72   6 / 10)60   4 / 12)48
7 / 7)49   10 / 10)100   6 / 8)48   3 / 12)36   7 / 8)56   12 / 10)120   Number Correct /20

Test 2—Dividing by 7 to 12

11 / 9)99   9 / 7)63   2 / 12)24   11 / 10)110   5 / 7)35   4 / 9)36   3 / 8)24
7 / 12)84   6 / 7)42   2 / 9)18   10 / 8)80   8 / 9)72   10 / 9)90   12 / 10)120
6 / 8)48   7 / 10)70   4 / 11)44   6 / 11)66   5 / 11)55   3 / 7)21   Number Correct /20

117

Test 3—Dividing by 7 to 12

10 / 7)70   1 / 10)10   12 / 12)144   4 / 8)32   6 / 11)66   3 / 10)30   5 / 10)50
12 / 7)84   12 / 9)108   6 / 7)42   8 / 9)72   3 / 10)30   4 / 7)28   5 / 12)60
6 / 8)48   6 / 9)54   11 / 11)121   7 / 8)56   9 / 8)72   5 / 9)45   Number Correct /20

Test 4—Dividing by 7 to 12

11 / 9)99   7 / 7)49   2 / 12)24   5 / 8)40   3 / 10)30   8 / 11)88   4 / 12)48
10 / 7)70   4 / 9)36   6 / 7)42   12 / 10)120   12 / 9)108   1 / 12)12   10 / 10)100
11 / 8)88   6 / 11)66   2 / 7)14   3 / 8)24   6 / 10)60   9 / 8)72   Number Correct /20

118

Test 5—Dividing by 7 to 12

6 / 9)54   3 / 7)21   2 / 8)16   10 / 8)80   9 / 10)90   6 / 8)48   7 / 10)70
4 / 12)48   5 / 11)55   7 / 8)56   11 / 7)77   11 / 11)121   8 / 7)56   1 / 9)9
10 / 10)100   2 / 9)18   5 / 12)60   9 / 9)81   9 / 11)99   12 / 12)144   Number Correct /20

Test 6—Dividing by 7 to 12

12 / 7)84   3 / 12)36   4 / 12)48   9 / 9)81   4 / 8)32   5 / 12)60   6 / 11)66
3 / 10)30   8 / 9)72   4 / 7)28   2 / 7)14   5 / 8)40   7 / 9)56   7 / 7)35
11 / 11)121   11 / 8)88   8 / 10)80   10 / 10)100   12 / 10)120   5 / 9)45   Number Correct /20

119

Test 7—Dividing by 7 to 12

3 / 12)36   5 / 7)35   4 / 9)36   4 / 12)48   8 / 7)56   10 / 12)120   6 / 7)42
6 / 8)48   7 / 9)63   5 / 12)60   5 / 10)50   4 / 11)44   12 / 10)120   11 / 8)88
12 / 7)84   9 / 10)90   9 / 9)81   10 / 8)80   6 / 9)54   3 / 10)30   Number Correct /20

Test 8—Dividing by 7 to 12

5 / 10)50   6 / 7)42   3 / 9)27   11 / 12)132   2 / 9)18   8 / 8)64   8 / 9)72
2 / 8)16   12 / 10)120   9 / 7)63   7 / 11)77   7 / 7)28   3 / 12)36   4 / 9)36
10 / 10)100   4 / 12)48   6 / 10)60   3 / 8)24   6 / 9)54   10 / 9)90   Number Correct /20

120

Test 9—Dividing by 7 to 12

8 / 11)88   6 / 7)42   6 / 8)48   3 / 9)27   7 / 7)49   6 / 11)66   5 / 12)60
2 / 8)16   5 / 10)50   11 / 9)99   6 / 10)60   1 / 7)7   3 / 8)24   10 / 7)70
7 / 11)77   3 / 7)21   8 / 9)72   12 / 12)144   8 / 8)64   4 / 10)40   Number Correct /20

Test 10—Dividing by 7 to 12

4 / 9)36   8 / 7)56   5 / 8)40   1 / 12)12   2 / 9)18   10 / 8)80   6 / 10)60
6 / 9)54   4 / 10)40   3 / 12)36   10 / 7)70   9 / 11)99   7 / 10)70   3 / 9)27
2 / 10)20   12 / 7)84   8 / 8)64   7 / 12)84   11 / 7)77   4 / 12)48   Number Correct /20

121

Test 1—Dividing by 1 to 12

5 / 5)25   4 / 8)32   3 / 5)15   10 / 3)30   9 / 11)99   12 / 6)72   9 / 3)27
1 / 2)2   8 / 2)16   10 / 12)120   10 / 6)60   7 / 8)56   7 / 9)63   4 / 4)16
9 / 7)63   5 / 7)35   11 / 3)33   12 / 1)12   10 / 4)40   5 / 10)50   Number Correct /20

Test 2—Dividing by 1 to 12

6 / 5)30   5 / 2)10   1 / 9)9   10 / 1)10   12 / 7)84   3 / 9)27   6 / 11)66
9 / 12)108   8 / 10)80   8 / 4)32   12 / 5)60   11 / 9)99   2 / 4)8   9 / 4)36
7 / 6)42   9 / 7)63   4 / 8)32   5 / 9)45   2 / 3)6   35 / 1)35   Number Correct /20

122

Test 3—Dividing by 1 to 12

9 / 5)45   11 / 1)11   9 / 3)27   3 / 4)12   8 / 7)56   1 / 7)7   12 / 10)120
10 / 2)20   6 / 1)6   12 / 2)24   9 / 9)72   5 / 8)40   10 / 8)80   3 / 12)36
10 / 10)100   1 / 6)6   6 / 5)30   7 / 6)42   12 / 9)108   6 / 11)66   Number Correct /20

Test 4—Dividing by 1 to 12

4 / 6)24   7 / 10)70   6 / 7)42   12 / 11)132   10 / 5)50   9 / 9)81   1 / 12)12
12 / 2)24   3 / 12)36   8 / 12)96   6 / 3)18   10 / 4)40   8 / 8)64   11 / 5)55
4 / 9)36   11 / 7)77   12 / 5)60   7 / 2)14   4 / 10)40   5 / 11)55   Number Correct /20

123

351

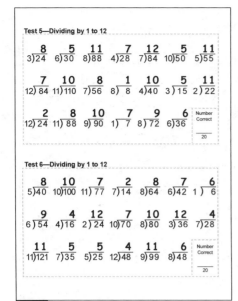

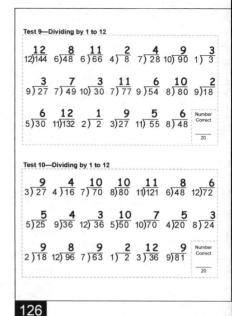

124   **125**   **126**

Grammar and Reading

Exploring Types of Sentences, p. 168
1. a) I have to do my homework now. I just finished reading my book. b) Did you know Jack was home? Have you washed the dishes yet? c) I saw that! You have got to be kidding! d) Close the window. Watch where you step!

Common Nouns vs. Proper Nouns, p. 169
1. a) common nouns: dog, doorbell; proper noun: Mike;
   b) common nouns: walk, beach; proper nouns: Anna, Cass;
   c) common nouns: mother, lunch; proper nouns: John, Sammy;
   d) common nouns: banana, toast, breakfast; proper noun: Tim;
   e) common nouns: pizza toppings, pepperoni, cheese, green peppers; proper nouns: Kim
2. a) common noun, b) proper noun, c) common noun, d) proper noun

Abstract Nouns, p. 170
1. a) courage, abstract noun, b) dog, common noun, c) imagination, abstract noun, d) friendship, abstract noun
2. Sample answers: a) Hope is better than despair. b) My friend has a great talent for singing. c) I am in good health.

Collective Nouns, p. 171
1. a) pack, b) deck, c) flock, d) crowd, e) team, f) bouquet, g) troupe
2. Sample answers: a) I saw a herd of cows. b) My brother has a collection of stamps.

Plural Nouns Review, p. 172
a) halves, b) teeth, c) feet, d) abilities, e) lives, f) toys, g) doors, h) women, i) wives, j) classes, k) sheep, l) wishes, m) quizzes, n) loaves, o) berries, p) dishes, q) witches, r) foxes, s) mice, t) stitches

Pronouns, p. 173
1) a) She, b) We, c) I, d) you, e) They, f) she, g) He, h) it, i) them, j) They

Object Pronouns, p. 174
1. a) her, b) it, c) me, d) us, e) us, f) him, g) them, h) it, i) you, j) them, k) it

Pronouns: *Me* vs. *I*, p. 175
1. a) I, b) me, c) I, d) me, e) I, f) me, g) me, h) I, i) me, j) I

Indefinite Pronouns: *Someone* and *Nobody*, p. 176
1. Sample answers: a) Nobody, b) Someone, c) Someone, d) nobody, e) someone, f) Nobody, g) someone, h) Nobody, i) someone, l) Nobody

Subordinate Clauses: What Are They? p. 177
1. a) I will take out the garbage if you come to the park with me. b) I got the best seat because I got there first. c) We will go to the movies when my aunt comes over. d) I will fail my test if I do not study. e) My dad will let me play outside after I do my chores. f) I can play with my puppy when I finish my homework.

Subordinate Conjunctions, p. 178
1. a) when, b) until, c) unless, d) because, e) when, f) while, g) since, h) once

Adverbs: Adverbial Phrases, p. 179
1. green adverbs: below, now, cheerfully, soon, better, brightly, south, yesterday, quickly, fast, easily, never, more, above, neatly, occasionally, north; blue adverbial phrases: as soon as, in the cupboard, in an hour, with ease, in a minute, in the classroom, a day ago, with difficulty

Verbs: Past, Present, and Future Tenses, p. 180
1. a) sang, past tense; b) will give, future tense; c) talked, past tense; d) eats, present tense

Exploring Commas, p. 181
1. a) I made a salad with lettuce, cucumber, and tomato. b) There is milk, cheese, and bread in the refrigerator. c) My teacher gave us math, reading, writing, and science for homework. d) June, July, August, and September are my favourite months. e) There were monkeys, giraffes, elephants, and jaguars at the zoo.

e Wise Chief and His Wife, p. 185

The chief was happy because he liked using his wisdom to solve difficult problems, and because he liked impressing the villagers with his wisdom.

The chief did not want people to think there was anyone in the village as wise as he was.

a) Shamika gave one of the boys an answer because she knew the boy had told the truth.

b) Possible answers include the following:
- Shamika believes strongly in honesty and fairness. She helped the boy who told the truth because it was only fair that the boy who stole the sheep should have to return it.
- Shamika is brave (or unselfish) because she knew that she was taking a risk in helping the boy, and she would have to return to her father's house if the chief found out.
- Shamika believes that sometimes breaking a rule is the right thing to do.

. Most students will likely believe that Shamika is wiser because she was able to figure out a way to make the chief forgive her and let her come back.

he Magic Mirror, p. 188

. The women were afraid that they had faults (or were aware that they had) and would probably be embarrassed or ashamed if they looked in the mirror and dark spots appeared. (Students might also mention that women would fear being publicly embarrassed—the crowd outside the barber's shop would realize that a woman had failed the test if she did not later marry the king.)

. A king usually wants to marry a woman who comes from a wealthy or noble family. Most kings would not marry a girl who worked tending sheep, even if she had no faults.

. a) The barber probably thought that the story about the mirror would be a good way to encourage a woman of good character to come forward, and to discourage women who knew that they did not have good character.

b) Students might suggest answers such as the following:
- If a woman knew that she did not have good character and was brave enough to look in the mirror, no spots would have appeared and she might have married the king.
- The king might have punished the barber if he found out the barber had lied to him about the mirror being magic.
- People might no longer trust the barber, since he had lied about the mirror.

. Students might suggest the following ideas:
- The girl was confident enough to look into the mirror.
- The girl was honest enough to admit that she sometimes made mistakes.
- The girl was loving and protective of her sheep; being loving and protective are good qualities for a wife and future mother.

Tryouts, p. 191

1. The story is told from Nia's point of view because she says "I" and "me" when she is telling her story.
2. She plays basketball in her driveway.
3. A *compress* is something cold or warm that you put on an injury to help it feel better faster.
4. *Shiner* refers to Nia's black eye.
5. Sample answer: It reminds me of a time in school when a girl punched me in the eye because I tickled her. I got a black eye from that, and a cut under my eye.
6. Nia displays determination when, despite her black eye and the teasing from the other girls, she kept trying her best, and managed to get on the basketball team.

Travelling to the Past, p. 193

1. The note said, "Happy birthday! I know you love history and adventure. Follow the instructions and you will have an out—of—this—world adventure. Have the 'time' of your life!" and "I know time flies when you are having fun, but remember to always be back in three hours."
2. Sample answer: I think Ellen's cousin sent her this present because she knows Ellen loves history and adventure, and travelling back in time would be like travelling into history. And that would definitely be an adventure!
3. Ellen travelled back to the time of Queen Elizabeth I, in 1590.
4. Ellen and Queen Elizabeth I discussed explorers, battling the Spanish, and how much fun it is to ride horses.
5. Answers will vary. You might wish to have students share with the class.
6. Sample answer: It means that time seems to go a lot faster when you are enjoying what you are doing.

Two Friends, Two Places, p. 196

1. Sam and Daniel are both originally from Toronto, Ontario.
2. Answers will vary. NOTE: Some students come from countries where there was conflict and war, so talking about where they came from can be a sensitive subject. If you would like students to share, ask for volunteers.
3. Vancouver is very rainy, and St. John's is cold, damp, and very windy.
4. From up on Signal Hill, Daniel can see the Atlantic Ocean, a few boats, and sometimes icebergs.
5. In Stanley Park, Sam loves to explore, walk on the beach. and pick up driftwood and rocks, too.
6. Answers will vary. You might wish to have students share with the class.
7. Sample answer: Daniel said his jaw dropped, so I think he was shocked and amazed.
8. "My jaw dropped" means that my mouth fell open because I was so shocked or amazed by something.
9. Answers will vary.

Blog or News? p. 198

1. The main idea is that there is a difference between a news article and a blog. The author supports this by giving an example of a news article and a blog about the same topic. This helps me understand the differences better.
2. The first item is a news article because it gives factual information and is announcing a new product. It is also more formal than the other article.
3. Sequel means something that comes after something else. *The Far Away Country* is a sequel to the first book, so it is a book that comes after the first book.
4. Formal writing sounds like writing you would find in a newspaper or a school book. Informal writing sounds as though you are talking to a friend.

5.

News Article	Both	Blog
• is all facts about the book, the author, the main character, and about the first book. • writing is more formal—you do not know who wrote the news article • does not give an opinion, it just gives information on buying the book • includes the price of the book and the age groups it is written for	• tell that the new book has arrived in stores • give a little information on the book and says that it is part of a series • give information on the author and her other book • tell a little about the story	• has some facts, such as the names of the two books, the author, and the main character. • is written in an informal way • gives the name of the writer of the blog • gives the writer's opinion of the book • shows that the writer wants people to read the book

Wayne Gretzky, p. 201

1.

Character Trait	Details from the Text
unselfish player	The most important thing to him was for his team to win. So he would pass the puck to a teammate who had the best chance to score.
determined	He practised four or five hours a day with his brothers.
enthusiastic	He learned everything he could about playing hockey from his dad.
smart	He always seemed to know where the puck was on the ice and what it would do. He would make the right play at the right time.

2. Answers will vary.

Idioms, p. 211

Answers might vary. Sample answers:
1. If I do not get my homework done again today, I will be in hot water with my parents.
2. I want to talk to the new kid in class, but every time I try, I get cold feet.
3. I had tons of homework, a project, chores, and a club meeting all on the same night, so I was a complete basket case.
4. Tell me all about your exciting trip to the mountains. I am all ears!
5. The great big package contained a tiny amount of pretzels, so it was a big rip-off.
6. If I do not pass my test, I will fail this class, and if I do, my goose is cooked!
7. I am so hungry after playing basketball all afternoon that I am going to pig out.
8. I was trying to keep the party a secret, but my little sister let the cat out of the bag.

Social Studies

Canada's National Symbols, p. 223

1. An *emblem* is a symbol that represents something.
2. As early as 1700, people began to use the maple leaf as a symbol of Canada. The country's Aboriginal peoples taught early European explorers and settlers how to make sweet syrup from the maple tree sap.
3. In World War I and World War II, Canada's fighters wanted a symbol that would remind them of their country because it would show that they were different from any other soldiers.
4. Canada chose its current red-and-white flag in 1965.
5. Canada's first postage stamp featured a beaver. Since the stamp cost 3 cents, it became known as the "Three Penny Beaver."
6. Answers will vary. Sample answer: Hockey is an important Canadian symbol because it is a sport that our country is very good at. Hockey and sports in general help bring us together as a country. Hockey is particularly important because it is a sport that embraces the climate of our country. It is a cold-weather sport, so we have the right weather in which to play it and to become very good at it. Canada has also won lots of international tournaments and Olympic medals in hockey. It is something for Canadians to be proud of.
7. You might wish to create a bulletin board display of students' stamp designs.

The Musical Ride, p. 227

1. The Musical Ride is an event in which a specially trained group of RCMP officers, or Mounties, perform intricate manoeuvres on horseback.
2. Sample answers:

Chacteristics	Reason
good-natured	it takes about 16 weeks of gruelling practice for the 32 riders and their horses to put together a Musical Ride show, so they have to be good natured or it would not be easy to train them
able to cope with constantly changing sights and sounds	to deal with parades, traffic, and crowds
all black	because they look so impressive with the Mounties' red coats

3. Between 785 and 788 RCMP officers who apply to take part in the Musical Ride are turned down each year.
4. It takes about 16 weeks to put together a Musical Ride show.
5. They must learn many patterns and figures, with names such as the Bridal Arch, the Wagon Wheel, Thread the Needle, and the Dome.
6. Just before the performance, each rider takes a wet brush and stencil and marks a maple leaf on their horse's rump.

The Great Lakes, p. 230

1. The acronym is HOMES and it stands for: Huron, Ontario, Michigan, Erie, Superior.
2. The largest Great Lake is Lake Superior. It is the largest inland lake anywhere on Earth.
3. Lake Huron was named by French explorers for the Huron Aboriginal peoples who lived in the area.
4. Ships moving grain and other supplies from Canada's prairies to countries in Europe are loaded in Thunder Bay, up on Lake Superior. They travel across Lake Superior, Lake Huron, and

Lake Erie, and bypass Niagara Falls by sailing through the Welland Canal. They finish their trip by sailing the length of Lake Ontario, then down the St. Lawrence River to the Atlantic Ocean.

. Most of the shipwrecks lie deep below the dark waters of Lake Huron, where the eastbound and the westbound shipping lanes cross. An area farther up in Lake Superior has become known as the "Graveyard of the Great Lakes."

. Lake Superior's Aboriginal name is *Gitchigumi*, which means "great lake." Lake Michigan's name comes from the Aboriginal word *mishigami*, which means "great water." Lake Ontario gets its name from an Aboriginal word that means "shining water."

. Lake Huron was named by French explorers for the Huron Aboriginal peoples who lived in the area. A neighbouring Aboriginal group also gave its name to Lake Erie.

Black Loyalists, p. 233

. In 1775, war broke out between the British and the Americans in the country now known as the United States.

. To attract more soldiers, the British promised land in Canada to all the black people who fought on their side. These people became known as the Black Loyalists.

3. The British offered them a farm in Canada, and promised them their freedom.

. Many Black Loyalists found Canada bitterly cold. Some left and sailed to Africa. Others moved elsewhere in Canada in hopes of finding better conditions.

. Some Black Loyalists waited six years before they received any land. Then they received only a tiny piece of land, much smaller than what they had been promised. The land was often rocky and far from the nearest town or water.

. Answers will vary. Sample: Black Loyalists stayed loyal to Britain. Despite this, Britain lost the battle. After the war, Britain quickly moved the Black Loyalists out of the United States. Some loyalists were captured into slavery. About 3,500 Black Loyalists were granted freedom. About half settled near Shelburne, Nova Scotia.

Gimli, Manitoba, p. 235

. Around 1875, natural disasters in Iceland left many people in the country with little to eat. Many Icelanders decided to leave their country, and a group of them chose to come to Canada.

. The Icelanders named their settlement after the Hall of Gimli, which is known as *paradise* in Norse and Viking myths.

. People from Germany, Hungary, Poland, and Ukraine, eventually moved into Gimli.

. Answers will vary. Sample answer: I think it is important to celebrate ethic cultures because it reminds Canadians where we came from. It helps remind us that we should be open to and accepting of different cultures, and learn to understand how other people live in different parts of the world.

. Answers will vary. Sample answer: In 1983, a pilot had to make an emergency landing in Gimli. The pilot knew there had once been an airport in Gimli, so he glided the plane down to land. The pilot did not know that the airport had been turned into a racetrack and that there was a race happening. Luckily the pilot was able to avoid hurting anyone and was able to safely land the plane.

6. The festival was first held in Winnipeg in 1890, and continued there until 1932, when it was moved to Gimli. It has been held in Gimli ever since.

Klondike Gold Rush, p. 238

1. Facts about the Chilkoot Pass include that it was the most famous part of the trek through the Coast Mountains, it was a staircase of 1,500 steps, it was too narrow for wagons or horses, miners had to carry their supplies and equipment on

their backs, the pass was covered with slippery ice in winter, workers cut steps in the ice, these steps became known as the "Golden Stairs," and about 1,500 women trekked through the Chilkoot Pass in long skirts.

2. The Gold Rush changed the Klondike by bringing many people to the area, making the area world-famous, pushing First Nations people aside and treating them badly, causing Dawson City to be set up, and changing how people saw Canada's Far North.

3. A *stampede* is a sudden rush of people or animals in response to something.

4. Sample answer: It was harder for women because they had to wear long, heavy skirts, as well as petticoats and corsets. It was harder for men because they had to carry huge packs of equipment and supplies up the slope, slide down, and haul up another batch. So it was hard for men and for women, just in different ways.

5. Answers might vary. Sample answer: Effects: First Nations peoples were pushed aside and badly treated during the Gold Rush, it changed how people saw Canada's far north, people realized it is more than a barren wasteland, the influx of so many people changed Yukon, Dawson City was set up in 1896 and was the centre of the Gold Rush and the capital of Yukon until 1952. The increased population also meant that the Northwest Territories were split up in 1898 and the new Yukon Territory (today, simply Yukon) was formed.

Home Children, p. 240

1. Home children were the many children in London, England, who were orphaned and homeless. Some groups decided these children would have a chance for a better life in Canada. The children who were sent to Canada became known as "home children."

2. They thought the clean air of Canada and a chance to work and earn some money would be wonderful for the children.

3. Sample answer: I agree with what the women did with the home children. They were looking out for the best interests of the children. Even though the program did not work out well, I think the intentions of the program were good.

4. Sample answer: I think the boy who said that meant he did not feel as though he was being treated like a person. He felt more like he was being treated like a working animal.

5. They did not have any of the freedoms that people should have. They were treated like servants, made to work hard, whipped and beaten, and some were starved.

6. The children did not have a choice about coming to Canada, or which jobs they would do when they got there.

7. Sample answer: I think that many home children did not return to England because they did not know anyone there. Many of these children were orphans when they left, so they had no family to return to England for. They must have found friends and family in Canada to stay with. They made Canada their new home.

8. Sample answer: I do not think it was fair that other people made money off of the home children's work. I think it was very greedy of the people in England to have forced the children to leave their home country, just so they could make more money. The home children did not gain any advantage from what happened to them.

Pier 21, p. 243

1. Most immigrants to Canada had to pass through inspection at Pier 21 before they were allowed to enter the country, so the facility became known as the "Gateway to Canada."

2. True.

3. *War brides* were women from many countries, but mostly from Britain, who met and married Canadian soldiers during the war.

4. In 1971, Pier 21 closed its doors. By then, most immigrants

were arriving in Canada by plane at the country's various international airports. Very few newcomers passed through Pier 21.

5. In 1999, Pier 21 reopened its doors, this time as the Canadian Museum of Immigration at Pier 21. There you can find out about the many brave immigrants who arrived at Pier 21.

6. Answers will vary. Sample: First, immigrants walked along the gangplank to the dock. Then they were examined by a doctor to make sure they were healthy and would not bring disease into Canada. If they were sick, they were quarantined. If they were not sick, they got to speak with an immigration official. This official decided whether they could stay in Canada. If they were allowed to stay, volunteers helped these new immigrants find food and shelter.

Why Immigrants Choose Canada, p. 245
You might wish to create a bulletin board display of students' collages.

1. Concept maps might vary
2. Answers might vary. You might wish to have students share with the class.

In Flanders Fields, p. 250
1. "In Flanders Fields" was such a successful poem because it captured how people were feeling at the time. It is not long, so people do not lose interest when reading it. It also sounds good when it is read out loud. There are powerful images in the poem, which people can see clearly. The poem starts quietly, builds to a strong climax, and ends solidly.
2. Answers will vary. Ensure students include an explanation as to why they liked the line.
3. John McCrae was a doctor in charge of the medical station that was in the middle of the battles happening in Flanders.
4. John McCrae showed his courage by taking part in a number of wars. He was brave enough to work close to where the fighting was taking place and he kept on working even when he was in danger.
5. These lines encourage future soldiers to be brave and to continue to fight. Even though the dead soldiers have had to stop battling, the poem urges the living soldiers to be strong and not give up.
6. A lark is a type of bird. I know this because the poem says that they sing and fly, things that birds do

Camp X, p. 253
1. Sample answer: It was important for Camp X to stay a secret because the enemy would have loved to destroy it. I know this because the text says, "While the conflict raged in Europe, the camp was top secret, since enemy spies would have loved to destroy it."
2. Possible answer: I think the author mentioned that Stephenson had only a Grade 6 education because he or she wanted us to know how smart Stephenson was and how much he was able to do even though he did not finish school. I also think he or she wanted the reader to know that everyone is gifted in their own way and can be smart even if they do not go to school.
3. Answers will vary.
4. Words that can describe spies include clever, stealthy, deadly, bold, courageous, fit, confident, close-mouthed, and quick-witted.
5. People think Intrepid was so important in World War II because he, and the spies he trained, figured out enemy code, forged documents, and sabotaged German experiments. Intrepid also set up a spy network.
6. Today, Camp X is a park that anyone can visit, and there is a museum nearby. Spies do not train there anymore, and it is no longer a secret.

Fathers of Confederation, p. 255
1. Answers will vary. You might wish to have students share with the class.
2. A *confederation* is a group of people or colonies that join together.
3. Joey Smallwood and Paul Okalik can be considered Fathers of Confederation because they worked hard to have their province or territory join Confederation, and after they joined, they were the first premiers.
4. Four provinces first joined Canada. The provinces were New Brunswick, Nova Scotia, (formerly Upper Canada), and Quebec (formerly Lower Canada).
5. Reasons the provinces united to form one country included that the United States were threatening to take them over, that Great Britain would no longer pay to defend the provinces, the provinces on their own were not growing quickly, it was difficult for people in one province to sell goods to people in other provinces and because of a lack of transportation between the colonies.

Biography of a Famous Canadian, p. 257
You might wish to have students share with the class.

Sir John A Macdonald, p. 260
Concept maps will vary.

Canadian Pacific Railway, p. 262
1. The railway was to stretch from the east coast to the west coast to unite Canada. It would also let people travel across the country and allow businesses and farmers to ship their goods across the country.
2. The railway workers were called "navvies"—they got their name from the men who had built water channels known as navigation canals.
3. These railway workers cut down trees and cleared a wide path, along the line the surveyors had marked. Then they used ploughs to level the ground for the tracks.
4. The government wanted to avoid building tunnels and bridges because these were more difficult, time-consuming, and expensive.
5. The railway wound through mountains and over rivers, which were extremely difficult to work around. Crews also used dynamite to tunnel through rock and it was dangerous work that killed many workers.
6. The first train chugged into the station at Port Moody, British Columbia, on July 4, 1886. It was the first passenger train to travel across the country.
7. Sample answer: First, survey crews headed out to find the best route for the railway. Then crews worked to lay the tracks. Then, work crews cleared the land. After the land was cleared, workers laid wooden railway ties across the roadbed. Then they placed a steel rail on each side of the ties. They hammered the rails into place with iron spikes, spread gravel and rock to secure the rails, then moved on to the next section until they finished the railway.

The Famous Five, p. 264
1. Sample answers: Fighting for the Right to Vote, Women Standing up for Their Rights
2. Facts about the Famous Five: they were well educated, they worked in Alberta, they wanted to improve life for Canadian women, they were strong and determined, they felt it was important that everyone was treated fairly and equally, they fought for a minimum wage for women, they fought for women's right to vote, they wanted to increase the rights of farm women, they were brought together by member Emily Murphy, and they fought to have women declared persons.

Emily Murphy was told she could not be a magistrate because she was a woman and so was not considered a person.

Possible answers: Nellie McClung felt it was important for women to vote because that would allow them to elect for politicians who supported women's rights, women would be recognized as important, men would care about their opinions, and women could vote for policies that would make their lives better.

Supreme means most important, or the highest in ranking.

If women could not vote, they would not have a way to let the government know about their wants and needs, and they would not have the same rights men have. Women would still not matter.

Old Money, New Money, p. 266

1. You might wish to ask a few students to share with the class.
2. People stopped using large stone doughnuts as money because they were too heavy to use easily.
3. "Put your money where your mouth is" means you stand by what you say.
4. Coins are made of metal, which lasts longer than paper. Coins do not have to be replaced as frequently as bills. This makes coins less expensive to produce and better for the environment.
5. Bills could be made of stronger materials with more detailed patterns on them. Coins could also have complex designs and be made of metals that are difficult to obtain.
6. You might wish to make a display of students' drawings.

Canada's Exports and Imports, p. 268

1. *Trade* is the importing and exporting of goods to and from other countries.
2. *Exports* are goods that are for sale or exchange from Canada to other countries.
3. Some of Canada's major exports include aluminum, precious metals, metal ores, newsprint, lumber, wood pulp, wheat, natural gas, petroleum, and technology.
4. *Imports* are goods that a country purchases from or trades for with other countries.
5. Some of Canada's major imports include cars, car parts, fruits, vegetables, and technology.
6. Answers will vary.

Cool Canadian Inventions, p. 270

1. Aboriginal peoples invented canoes, toboggans, and snowshoes. Inuit inventors even created sunglasses to make it easier to see when snow reflects bright sunshine.
2. In 1922, Joseph-Armand Bombardier invented the snowmobile to make it easier to get around in winter in Canada's north.
3. The anti-gravity suit and the Canadarm went into space.
4. Canadians invented the Jolly Jumper for babies, the tabletop hockey game, IMAX films, basketball, five-pin bowling, and synchronized swimming.
5. Peter L. Robertson invented a square-headed screwdriver— which became known as the Robertson screwdriver—and screws with a square socket on them.
6. Sample answer: Since the electron microscope allows people to see tiny things that had been invisible to the human eye, doctors can now identify difference viruses and bacteria so they know how to treat a sick patient.
7. John Hopps of Toronto invented the pacemaker in 1950. This device sends pulses of electricity to a person's heart to make it beat regularly.
8. Sample answer: An artificial heart might act like a real heart and take over pumping blood in a person's body.

Science

Living Things, p. 272

1. Sample answer: A rabbit is a living thing because it is made up of many cells. It drinks water and eats things such as plants and grasses. It gets energy from eating and drinking so it can grow from a baby rabbit into an adult rabbit. It breathes air so it can get oxygen. It reacts to its environment by running away from animals that might eat it. Rabbits can reproduce.
2. gold ring: rock; cheese: milk from a cow or goat; paper: tree; wool scarf: sheep; glass jar: silica; No items are living.
3. Sample answer: Robins dig in the ground for earthworms and insects. They eat berries off bushes. They drink water from puddles.
4. Temperature is part of habitat. A habitat provides an organism with things it needs to survive. A suitable temperature is one of those things.

Classifying Organisms, p. 274

1. The most common classification system divides organisms into these five kingdoms: Plantae, Animalia, Fungi, Monera, Protista.
2. If scientists used different classification systems, it would be difficult to share information.
3. Sample answer:

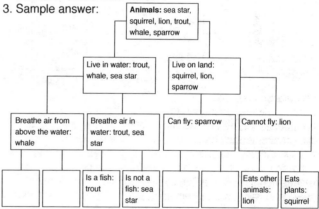

The Animal Kingdom, p. 276

1. Because it has the same characteristics as all animals: it is multicellular, eats other organisms, such as flies, moves by itself, and lays eggs to reproduce.
2. Sample answer: Vertebrates are easier to see.
3. Because they all have jointed legs and exoskeletons.
4. Wings
5. Sample answer:

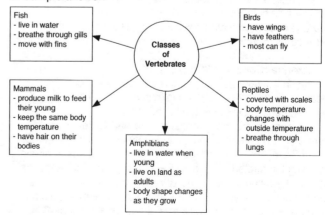

The Forgotten Kingdoms, p. 278
1. Sample answer:

	Cell structure	Getting nutrition	Examples of organisms	Habitat	What they do or how they affect us
Monera	- unicellular - most basic cell structure	- absorb nutrients from outside their bodies	- bacteria	- everywhere - in air, soil, water, extreme temperatures, and harsh chemical environments	- turn milk into cheese and yogurt - keep us healthy - make us sick - decompose waste - help make medicines
Protista	- mostly unicellular - more complex cell structure than monerans	- some make their own food - some absorb nutrients - some consume other organisms	- algae - amoebas - slime moulds	- mostly in water - in damp soil - in animal bodies	- cause diarrhea and stomach upset - one causes malaria - algae are at the bottom of the food pyramid
Fungi	- mostly multicellular	- feed on dead plants and animals	- mushrooms - toadstools - mildews - moulds - truffles - yeast	- most live on land in dark, moist places	- produce antibiotics - we eat some types - cause diseases in people and plants - used for baking

Biodiversity, p. 280
1. Both are classified according to characteristics and start with large groups that are divided into smaller and smaller groups.
2. Ensure that students' brochures include the worldwide locations, climate, plant and animal life, an example of a food chain, and interesting facts about their chosen biome.
3. Sketches might include a variety of deciduous trees, small bushes, and wildflowers. Animals might include deer, raccoons, foxes, and birds. Non-living features include water, air, and rocks.
4. Both communities contain living and non-living things. The living things interact with each other and help each other. The living things depend on other living things for food. They also depend on non-living things for shelter, tools, and other things they need.
5. Sample answers: Our quality of life depends on biodiversity. We get many things from our environment: food products, timber, fresh water, clean air, and medicines. Also, healthy communities help regulate our climate and pollinate our crops. They also provide us with beautiful landscapes and recreational areas.

Species Interactions, p. 282
1. Corn is on the bottom because it is a plant. The mouse is next because it eats the corn. The snake is next because it eats the mouse. The hawk is at the top because it eats the snake.
2. a) Commensalism. The weed gets to spread its seeds and reproduce. The organism that carries the burrs is not affected. b) Mutualism. The bacteria get food. The human gets to digest food with the bacteria's help. c) Parasitism. The deer tick gets food, and the animal gets bitten and loses blood.
3. Sample answer: New species might kill off existing species. Organisms that ate that species would suffer and might die off too. The invasive species might have no predators in the new area, so the population may increase rapidly. There might be

so many of the invasive species that the habitat is unable to support them. Then the habitat will change and this will affect all the other organisms.

Medicine from Plants, p. 284
1. a) white willow tree, iii) aspirin; b) foxglove, iv) digitalis; c) fever tree, i) quinine; d) aloe, ii) alonin
2. The rubber tree does not provide us with medicine, but rather things such as rubber gloves and waterproof sheeting, which are important parts of health care and medicine.
3. For thousands of years, people have relied on plants for food, building materials, medicine, and rubber for making rubber gloves, plastic sheeting, tires, etc. The five plant parts people use are the roots, leaves, flowers, bark, and berries.
4. *Rely* means "to depend on something or someone."
5. Sample answer: If people do not protect the plants where they live and the plants die, we could be losing a source of potentially life-saving medicine.

Adaptations, p. 286
1. Sample answer: Dandelions have a long root that goes straight into the ground. This makes it difficult to pull them out. It can regrow from any root pieces left behind. Porcupines have strong claws that help them dig for food.
2. a) Sheltered from hot weather
   b) Can use its front teeth underwater without swallowing water
   c) Can see above the water when most of its body is hidden underwater
3. Drawings might address adaptations related to gathering/hunting food, movement, and self-defence.

Cougars vs. Lynxes—What Is the Difference? p. 288
1. The cougar is bigger and it has the longer tail.
2. Lynxes' paws are larger than human hands.
3. When hunting, the lynx lies in wait for prey to come close, then pounces. The cougar is speedy over short distances, and can easily chase down prey.
4. Lynxes eat mostly snowshoe hares, but will also hunt small- to medium-sized animals and birds. Cougars are much bigger, so they eat animals as large as deer, elk, and moose.
5. A crevice is a narrow opening or crack in a rock or wall.
6. Lynxes and cougars hunt at night because they have large eyes to see well in the dark and it is easier to sneak up on prey at night.

Leafcutter Ants, p. 290
1. Leafcutter ants crawl in long lines far into the forest to harvest leaves, they leave a scent along the trail to find their way back, they use their strong jaws to cut leaves from plants, then they carry the leaf chunks over their backs back to the nest. They then chew the leaf chunks into a pulp and store it with fungus spores in underground chambers. They add their droppings as fertilizer, then harvest the fungus that grows.
2. Humans form larger, more complex societies.
3. *Decaying* means rotting.
4. Leafcutter ants can strip the leaves off trees. They can also damage roads and farmland with their nest-building activity.
5. The farmers collect debris and garbage from a leafcutter ant nest and place it around the crops or seedlings that they want to protect. This keeps the leafcutter ants away for up to 30 days.

Up in the Air, p. 292
1. Sample timeline:
   1500 – Famous artist and inventor Leonardo da Vinci drew flying machines, but never built any of them.

1783 – Joseph and Étienne Montgolfier launched the world's first hot-air balloon.

1849 – George Cayley launched a glider that carried a 10-year-old boy a short distance.

1854 – George Cayley convinces a carriage driver to fly in his latest model. After the flight, the driver quits working for Cayley.

1896 – German engineer Otto Lilienthal has made about 2,000 glider flights by 1896.

1903 – The Wright brothers became the first people to fly in a controlled and powered aircraft. The plane was called Flyer. You might wish to create a bulletin board display of students' drawings.

It means that every inventor before the Wright brothers flew without control of their craft and without power to move it. They were basically gliding or sailing along.

Answers will vary. You might wish to have students share with the class.

5. The inventors based their ideas on birds that they watched soaring and flying in the sky.

Flying Through the Sky, p. 295

1. The flap changes the shape of the wing, so there is more drag.
2. Flat, so there will be less drag.
3. Flaps are tilted up on one wing and down on the other so that wind pushes each wing in opposite directions.
4. A bird could push the back of its wings down to increase drag and slow itself down.
5. Thrust

Experiment: Build an Aircraft, p. 297

Findings will vary. Look for evidence that students have applied and/or assessed the forces of flight on their aircraft.

Aircraft with Motors, p. 298

1. Sample answer: A helicopter does not need a runway. A helicopter can also hover and manoeuvre more precisely.

Animal Fliers, p. 299

1. A lighter animal has less weight to overcome when they fly.
2. Insects: can turn their wings; Bats: flap their spread-out fingers to fly; Birds: flap their wings to propel them through the air.

Furred and Finned Fliers, p. 300

1. Sample answer: light materials, large wings, a powerful launch device, flaps for steering

Amelia Earhart, p. 301

1. The main idea of the article is to inform readers about the amazing bravery of Amelia Earhart, the first woman to pilot a plane across the Atlantic Ocean.
2. Earhart was the first woman to be carried across the ocean in a plane, and the first woman to fly solo across the Atlantic Ocean.
3. Answers will vary.
4. Sample answer: It means that she did not think what she did was important enough for people to make that much of a fuss about it. It shows me that she was a humble person and that she did not make things in her life bigger than they really were.
5. Answers will vary. Sample answer: Earhart and Noonan might have crashed into the ocean, or died on an island somewhere in the Pacific Ocean.
6. Answers will vary.

Current and Static Electricity, p. 304

1. flashlight, power lines in a house, solar calculator, light switch
2. a) opposite
   b) same
3. Clothes rub together in the dryer, creating friction and building up charge. Pieces of clothing with opposite charges will stick together.

Experiment: Electric Cereal, p. 305

1. Expected results:
   5. a) When the comb got close to the cereal, the cereal swung to touch the comb and stuck to it.
   5. b) The cereal swung away from the comb.
   6. As the comb got closer to the cereal, the cereal moved away from the comb.
2. Friction creates a charge on the comb when it is rubbed against the wool.
3. This is static electricity, since the energy does not flow along a path.
4. Test whether a comb attracts the cereal if it is not rubbed on wool, or test a different type of cereal.

Using Water to Produce Electricity, p. 307

1. a) Unhappy, since their land will be flooded.
   b) May be happy for a new lake to use, or unhappy at the loss of the river.
   c) Happy for the new jobs during construction.
   d) Unhappy because of the threat of flooding if an earthquake damages the dam.
2. Answers will vary. Look for supported arguments.

Using Wind to Produce Electricity, p. 309

1. The lighter the blades, the less wind is needed to make them turn. A wind turbine with very light blades will be able to produce electricity when the wind is not very strong. Heavier blades require stronger wind to make them turn.
2. Mining for metal and the rocks required for concrete can pollute the environment and spoil the natural beauty of the landscape. Changing ore from the mine into metal parts for the wind turbine creates pollution. Energy is required to produce the metal parts and the concrete, and this energy may be produced in ways that create pollution.

3.

Similarities	Differences
- produce electricity - use natural, renewable sources of energy - have a turbine with blades - use a generator with moving magnets and copper coils - produce electricity	- hydroelectric power plants use the energy of moving water; wind turbines use the energy of moving air - hydroelectric power plants must be built near water; wind turbines must be in windy areas that are flat and open - wind turbines can be dangerous for flying animals; hydroelectric power plants create hazards for people, and barriers to wildlife such as fish - hydro dams flood large areas of land and change the flow of the river; wind turbines do not change the landforms or waterways

Our Sun Is a Star, p. 311

1. The Sun's heat warms the Earth, powers the rain cycle, and creates wind. Sunlight makes plants grow, which provides us with food and oxygen.

Brain Stretch

Posters will vary. Make sure students' posters include diagrams and labels.

Planets in Our Solar System, p. 312

1. The planets closest to the Sun have three moons altogether.
2. Mars has the highest-known mountain.
3. Venus is the hottest planet.
4. Mercury is the smallest planet.
5. Jupiter is the largest planet.
6. Earth is the densest.
7. Mercury has the greatest daily temperature change.
8. Uranus spins on its side.
9. a) Mercury iii) peppercorn
   b) Venus v) black bean or vii) pea
   c) Earth v) black bean or vii) pea
   d) Mars vi) kernel of corn
   e) Jupiter ii) gum ball or iv) large marble
   f) Saturn ii) gum ball or iv) large marble
   g) Uranus i) small numbered cube or viii) small marble
   h) Neptune i) small numbered cube or viii) small marble

Moons, p. 315

1. Diagrams should show that the Moon is in the darkest part of Earth's shadow.
2. a) From Earth, the angle at which we observe the Moon's sunlit side changes, meaning we see less or more of the Moon.
   b) The Moon phases are already in order but students may start their observation at any point along the set, affecting where #1 starts.

They Came from Outer Space, p. 317

1. From largest to smallest: asteroids, meteoroids, comets.
2. Sample answer: Perseids are a group of meteors that we see streaking across the sky (like a shower) in the area where the Perseid constellation is found.

Astronauts and Space Travel, p. 318

1. Sample answer: Food, air, and water because there is none in space; computer with photos of friends, music player, e-book reader, and Internet access for entertainment, keeping and analyzing records, and communication; therapy bands for resistance exercise; sleeping bag because blankets would not stay in place while sleeping; ear plugs to block out others' sounds; and tools to fix things.
2. Sample answer: protection from the airless, cold, radiation-filled outer space; storage for supplies (including food) and waste (dirty clothes, human waste, food packaging, etc.); exercise area; sleeping and bathroom spaces; a place and equipment to perform experiments; communication with Earth; windows.

Space Technology, p. 320

1. Answers will vary. Look for reasoned arguments.
2. a) Fresh vi) Food is not preserved, so it must be eaten quickly.
   b) Intermediate Moisture ii) Food has some water removed; water is not replaced before eating.
   c) Irradiated iii) Food is cooked and packed in foil pouches. It is sterilized by radiation so it can be kept at room temperature.
   d) Natural v) Food is ready to eat and stored in flexible pouches.
   e) Rehydratable i) Food is freeze-dried to remove water. Water is replaced before eating.
   f) Thermostabilized iv) Food is heated to kill bacteria so it can be stored at room temperature.
3. Similarities include the confined space and need for life support.

It Came from Space, p. 322

1. Sample answer: Humans have been on Earth for thousands of years, but humans have only been travelling to space since 1957.
2. It might be important to do a blood analysis in 30 seconds if a patient is extremely ill and has a chance of dying if the doctors do not figure out what is wrong quickly.
3. A *spinoff* is a product that is developed as a result of another product that has already been developed and been used for some time.
4. Sample answer: Since the Moon is a satellite and it is from nature, an artificial satellite is probably something not from nature that orbits around Earth.
5. The main idea is that a lot of the technologies we use in everyday life were spinoffs of, or developed from, technologies used in space. The author supports this with lots of examples.
6. Sample answer: I think the author thinks these new technologies are good because the text says, "All of these technologies and many more help make our lives better."

On the Job with an Iceberg Wrangler, p. 324

1. Iceberg Alley is an area off the east coast of Newfoundland where icebergs float down from Baffin Bay on the Labrador Current.
2. Iceberg wranglers can move icebergs by putting a rope around them and towing them to change their direction, or by using a water cannon to blast them with water to get them moving in a different direction.
3. Sample answer: It is important to move icebergs out of the way of rigs and ships because the iceberg might crash into them and destroy them or sink them, like the Titanic.
4. *Pressure* is a continuous physical force that is applied to an object by something pressing or pushing against it.
5. Answers will vary.
6. Answers will vary.

What Does an Engineer Do? p. 328

1. Answers will vary. You might wish to have students share with the class.
2. Engineers are people who build all types of things that make our world work better. Many of the things you see and use every day were created by engineers. Some engineers work with chemicals to create new textiles, more flexible plastics, and stronger building materials. Others work in cities to build roads, bridges, and skyscrapers. Some engineers make medical supplies for hospitals, technology for space travel, and find new and safer ways to clean up the environment.